Printed in West Germany

The Arts of Thailand

A Handbook of the Architecture, Sculpture and Painting of Thailand (Siam), and a Catalogue of the Exhibition in the United States in 1960-61-62

INDIANA UNIVERSITY, BLOOMINGTON

THE METROPOLITAN MUSEUM OF ART, NEW YORK

MUSEUM OF FINE ARTS, BOSTON

THE TOLEDO MUSEUM OF ART, TOLEDO

LOS ANGELES COUNTY MUSEUM, LOS ANGELES

SEATTLE ART MUSEUM, SEATTLE

CALIFORNIA PALACE OF THE LEGION
OF HONOR, SAN FRANCISCO

HONOLULU ACADEMY OF ARTS, HONOLULU

EDITOR: THEODORE BOWIE

CONTRIBUTORS: ALEXANDER B. GRISWOLD

                        M. C. SUBHADRADIS DISKUL

                        ELIZABETH LYONS

DESIGNER: CARL F. ZAHN

PHOTOGRAPHS: NIPHON NIMBOONCHAJ

                        EWING KRAININ

                        A. B. GRISWOLD

                        ARCHAEOLOGICAL SURVEY OF THAILAND

                        PUBLIC RELATIONS DEPARTMENT, BANGKOK

@ @

Committee of Participating Institutions
and Dates of Exhibition

@ @

INDIANA UNIVERSITY, Bloomington, Indiana   October 9 to November 22, 1960
    Herman B Wells, *President*
    Henry R. Hope, *Chairman, Department of Fine Arts*

THE METROPOLITAN MUSEUM OF ART, New York   January 10 to February 19, 1961
    James J. Rorimer, *Director*
    Alan Priest, *Curator of the Far Eastern Department*

MUSEUM OF FINE ARTS, Boston   March 12 to April 23, 1961
    Perry T. Rathbone, *Director*
    Kojiro Tomita, *Curator of Asiatic Art*

THE TOLEDO MUSEUM OF ART, Toledo, Ohio   May 14 to June 11, 1961
    Otto Wittmann, *Director*

LOS ANGELES COUNTY MUSEUM   July 9 to August 13, 1961
    Jean Delacour, *Director*
    George Kuwayama, *Curator of Oriental Art*

SEATTLE ART MUSEUM   September 10 to October 8, 1961
    Richard E. Fuller, *President and Director*

CALIFORNIA PALACE OF THE LEGION OF   November 5 to December 17, 1961
    HONOR, San Francisco
    Thomas Carr Howe, Jr., *Director*

ACADEMY OF ARTS, Honolulu, Hawaii   January 21 to March 3, 1962
    Robert P. Griffing, Jr., *Director*

Committee of Selection

THAI
Dhanit Yupho, *Director General of Fine Arts*
M. C. Subhadradis Diskul, *Chief Curator of the National Museum, Bangkok*

AMERICAN
Kojiro Tomita, *Museum of Fine Arts, Boston*
Alexander B. Griswold, *Monkton, Maryland*
Theodore Bowie, *Indiana University (Chairman)*

ⓔ ⓔ

Introduction

ⓖ ⓖ

MUSEUMS have existed for a long time past as educational institutions for the intellectual information of communities and their visitors. The idea, however, of using museums as a means of promoting international understanding and encouraging peace in the world is more recent. It was with this in view that such an institution as the International Council of Museums came into being with the support of the United Nations Organisation through UNESCO.

It should therefore be a matter of great satisfaction to the intellectual world – and in fact to the world at large – to welcome this exhibition in the United States of selected works of art, the property of the Thai museums and of private persons or institutions both Thai and American, which will be circulated and displayed in the sponsoring institutions under the joint patronage of the respective chiefs of state, namely His Majesty the King of Thailand and His Excellency the President of the United States of America.

DHANI NIVAT
KROMAMÜN BIDYALABH

President of the Privy Council;
President of the Siam Society;
Former Regent of the Kingdom.

Bangkok, 25th May 1960

Acknowledgements

IT IS A MATTER of great pride for Indiana University to be associated with the National Museum of Bangkok and seven leading American Museums in bringing to the United States an Exhibition of the Arts of Thailand. An enterprise of such scope is not only proof of our faith in the value of cultural exchange on an international basis, it is evidence also of the passion we as a nation have for becoming acquainted with the arts of all lands. Circulating exhibitions, remaining for appreciable lengths of time in some of the main centers of culture across our land, afford opportunities for prolonged and repeated enjoyment of the masterpieces of all countries and every epoch. In the last fifteen years there have been enormous movements of artistic treasures from one continent to another, to the lasting delight of all visitors. The present Exhibition is merely the latest one in an Asian series which began in 1953 with the importation of works of Japanese Painting and Sculpture and which continued with the Masterpieces of Korean Art in 1957. This series will be climaxed but not ended with the announced tour, beginning in 1961, of the treasures of Chinese Art now housed on Taiwan.

Long in preparation and, like its predecessors, complex in its arrangements, the present undertaking has enjoyed the support of many official and unofficial bodies, public servants, and private persons, whose contributions in terms of money, services and indispensable advice are now publicly acknowledged.

The United States Department of State has supported the project from its inception and has made a grant in support of one Thai curator and his replacement for the entire duration of the Exhibition. The Asia Foundation of San Francisco, through its President, Mr. Robert Blum, has matched that subsidy in support of a second Thai curator and his substitute, for an equivalent period.

The United States Navy has cooperated to the extent of transporting the Exhibition and the curators overseas both ways.

The Rockefeller Foundation has made two grants, one in aid of the expenses of the American Committee of Selection, and another towards general administrative expenses. Mr. John D. Rockefeller, 3d, has made a generous and unrestricted personal grant.

Miss Ardelia R. Hall, Arts and Monuments Adviser to the Secretary of State, has been a source of advice and help during all the phases of planning and the intricate negotiations involving two Governments and a dozen public or semi-public institutions. Special thanks for technical and administrative advice are also due Mr. E. James Adams, Assistant Secretary of the National Gallery.

Three participating Museums have earned special gratitude for allowing members of their staffs to contribute distinctive services: the Metropolitan Museum of Art, whose Secretary, Mr. Dudley T. Easby, Jr., has acted as legal and administrative adviser of the project; the Boston Museum of Fine Arts, which permitted its Curator of Asiatic Art, Mr. Kojiro Tomita, to function as a valued member of the American Committee of Selection, and its Designer, Mr. Carl Zahn, to take charge of designing and supervising the production of the Catalogue; and, finally, the Honolulu Academy of Arts, which sent its expert packer, Mr. Walter Fraine, to plan and supervise the packing of the Exhibition in Bangkok.

The aid given by Mr. U. Alexis Johnson, United States Ambassador to Thailand, and the staff of the U. S. Information Service in Bangkok was of incalculable value. Particular acknowledgment must be made of the devoted services of Mr. Donald H. Rochlen, Cultural Exchange Officer, both in facilitating the work of the Committee of Selection and in the preparation of the Catalogue. Acknowledgement must also be made of the help given by Mr. Harry Pierson, The Asia Foundation representative in Bangkok.

The cordial cooperation and the generous hospitality of Thai officials and private individuals during all the stages of the project are gratefully remembered. Particular thanks go to M. L. Pin Malakul, Minister of Education, to Mr. Dhanit Yupho, Director-General of Fine Arts, to M. C. Subhadradis Diskul, Chief Curator of the Bangkok Museum, and to Mr. Bhunthin Attagora of the Ministry of Education. The kindness of the Bureau of Public Relations of Thailand in supplying photographs is also acknowledged. Professor Carlo Feroci is to be especially thanked for preparing material for use in the Catalogue.

Miss Elizabeth Lyons, of New York and Bangkok, has not only made a contribution to the Catalogue but has consistently placed her intimate familiarity with the artistic resources of Thailand at the disposal of the organizers. As for Mr. Alexander B. Griswold, of Bangkok and Monkton, Maryland, his services as member of the Committee of Selection, as author of a major part of the Catalogue and as general adviser to the project from the very beginning, can never be adequately recognized.

At Indiana University the advice and help of Professors Henry R. Hope, Walter Laves, Willis P. Porter and Joseph L. Sutton, and the never-failing encouragement and administrative aid given by Mr. A. Peter Fraenkel, Assistant to the President, Mr. T. E. Randall, Assistant Treasurer, and Mr. J. W. Hicks, Controller, are duly appreciated.

For more than five years Professor Theodore Bowie, of the Department of Fine Arts of Indiana University, has most patiently and energetically devoted himself to the good cause of the Exhibition. As organizer of the project, Director of the Exhibition and Editor of the Catalogue, Professor Bowie has earned the thanks of all those who will enjoy the Exhibition of the Arts of Thailand.

HERMAN B WELLS
President of Indiana University

@ @

Honorary Patrons

HIS MAJESTY THE KING OF THAILAND

HER MAJESTY THE QUEEN OF THAILAND

THE HONORABLE DWIGHT D. EISENHOWER,
President of the United States of America

AND MRS. EISENHOWER

6 6 6 6 6 6 6 6 6 6 6 6 6 6 6 6 6 6 6 6 6 6 6 6 6 6 6 6 6 6 6 6 6

Patrons

@ @

FOR THE KINGDOM OF THAILAND

HIS HIGHNESS PRINCE DHANI NIVAT
President of the Privy Council of Thailand

HIS EXCELLENCY
FIELD MARSHAL SARIT THANARAT
Prime Minister of Thailand

HIS ROYAL HIGHNESS
PRINCE WAN WAITHAYAKON
Deputy Prime Minister of Thailand

HIS EXCELLENCY THANAT KHOMAN
Minister of Foreign Affairs of Thailand

HIS EXCELLENCY M. L. PIN MALAKUL
Minister of Education of Thailand

PRINCESS CHUMBHOT OF NAGARA SVARGA

HIS EXCELLENCY VISUTR ARTHAYUKTI
*Ambassador of Thailand to the
United States of America*

MR. DHANIT YUPHO
*Director General of the
Fine Arts Department of Thailand*

M. R. KÜKRIT PRAMOJ

FOR THE UNITED STATES OF AMERICA

THE HONORABLE CHRISTIAN A. HERTER
*Secretary of State of the United States
of America*

THE HONORABLE THOMAS S. GATES, JR.
*Secretary of Defense of the United States
of America*

THE HONORABLE ARTHUR S. FLEMMING
*Secretary of Health, Education and Welfare
of the United States of America*

THE HONORABLE U. ALEXIS JOHNSON
*Ambassador of the United States to the
Kingdom of Thailand*

MR. ROBERT BLUM

MR. KENNETH P. LANDON

MR. JOHN D. ROCKEFELLER, 3D

MR. FRANCIS B. SAYRE *(Phya Kalyan Maitri)*

MR. EDWIN F. STANTON

Lenders to the Exhibition

H. M. THE KING OF THAILAND

H.R.H. PRINCE BHANUBANDHU YUGALA, BANGKOK

H.R.H. PRINCESS CHUMBHOT OF NAGARA SVARGA, BANGKOK

PRINCE PIYARANGSIT RANGSIT, BANGKOK

PRINCE SANID PRAYURASAKDI RANGSIT, BANGKOK

THE CHITRABONGS FAMILY, BANGKOK

THE PARIBATRA FAMILY, BANGKOK

HIS LORDSHIP THE ABBOT OF THE CETIYA LUANG MONASTERY, CHIENG MAI

HIS LORDSHIP THE ABBOT OF THE MONASTERY OF THE FIFTH KING, BANGKOK

HIS LORDSHIP THE ABBOT OF THE BODHI-TREE MONASTERY, BANGKOK

MR. ALEXANDER B. GRISWOLD, TONBURI

MRS. CONNIE MANGSKAU, BANGKOK

MR. KRAISRI NIMMANAHEMINDA, CHIENG MAI

MR. DHATA SAMPATI, BANGKOK

MR. ADHARA ŚIRIKANDARAVARA, BANGKOK

MR. JAMES H. W. THOMPSON, BANGKOK

THE NATIONAL MUSEUM, BANGKOK

THE VAÑIRAYĀN LIBRARY, BANGKOK

THE DEPARTMENT OF FINE ARTS (Musical Division), BANGKOK

THE NATIONAL MUSEUM, AYUDHYA

THE NATIONAL MUSEUM, LAMPUN

THE NATIONAL MUSEUM, LOPBURI

THE NATIONAL MUSEUM, NAGARA PATHAMA

Contents

Alternative Spellings of Place Names

GRAPHIC	PHONETIC	OTHER
Ayudhyā	Ayuttayâ	Ayuthya
Bejrapurī	Petburî	Petcha Buri
Bejrapūrṇa	Petchabûn	Phetchaboon
Bicitra	Pijit	Phichit
Bimāya	Pimâi	
Bishṇuloka	Pitsnulók	Phitsanulok
Braḥ Vihāra	Pra Wihân	Phra Viharn
Puriramya	Buriram	
Candapurī	Jantaburî	Chanthaburi
	Chieng Mai	Chiangmai
	Chieng Râi	Chiangrai
	Chieng Sèn	Chiangsaen
	Dâk	Tak
Dhanapurī	Tonburî	Dhonburi
Jaiyā	Chaiyâ	Xaiya
Jalapurī	Chonburî	
Jayabhūmi	Chaiyapûm	Chaiyaphoom
Jayanāda	Chainât	
Kālasindhu	Gâlasin	Kalasin
Kāṃbèng Bejra	Gampèng Pet	Kamphaengphet
Kañcanapurī	Ganburî	Kanchana Buri
Labpurī	Lopburî	
	Lambâng	Lampang
	Lampûn	Lamphoon
	Löi	Loei
Mahāsaragāma	Mahâ Sarakâm	Maha Sarakham
Nagara Bnam	Nakòn Pnom	Nakhon Phanom

GRAPHIC	PHONETIC	OTHER
Nagara Paṭhama	Nakòn Btom	Nakorn Pathom
Nagara Rājasimā	Kórât	Nakhon Ratchasima
Nagara Śri Dharmarāja	Nakòn Sî Tammarât	Nakhon Sidhammarat
Nagara Svarga	Nakòn Swan	Nakorn Sawan
	Nân	Nan
	Nòng Kai	Nongkhai
	Payao	Phayao
	Pong Dük	Phong Tu'k
Prācīṇapurī	Brâjînburî	Prachinburi
Rājapurī	Râtburî	
Sakalanagara	Sgon Nakòn	Sakon Nakhon
Samudraprākāra	Smut Brâgân	Samut Prakarn
Siṅhapurī	Singburi	
	Song Klâ	Song Khla
Srapurī	Srapburî	Sraburi
Śrī Deb	Sî Tép	
Śrī Sakesha	Sî Sgét	Sisaket
Sukhodaya	Sukkótai	Sukhothai
Subarṇapurī	Supan Burî	Suphanburi
Surashṭradhānī	Surat Tānī	Surat Thani
Surindra	Surin	
Svargaloka	Swankalók	Sawankhalok
Upalarājadhānī	Ubon	Ubon Ratcha Thani
Uttaradhānī	Udòn	Udon Thani
Uttaratittha	Uttaradit	
	Ŭ Tòng	Uthong

Abbreviations

AMD   Dupont, *Archéologie mône de Dvāravatī* (Paris, 1959).

BAS   leMay, *Buddhist Art in Siam* (Cambridge, 1938).

BEFEO Bulletin de l'Ecole Française d'Extréme Orient

BK   Coedès, *Bronzes khmèrs,* Ars Asiatica, Vol. V (Paris, 1923).

CSEA leMay, *Culture of South-East Asia* (London, 1954).

DBINS Griswold, *Dated Buddha Images of Northern Siam* (Ascona, 1957).

EOL   Etudes d'Orientalisme Linossier. (Paris, 1932)

JSS   Journal of the Siam Society

MNB   Coedès, *Collections archéologiques du Musée National de Bangkok,* Ars Asiatica, Vol. XII (Paris, 1928).

SVT   Coedès, *Siamese Votive Tablets,* JSS, Vol. XX/1 (Bangkok, 1926). (Translation of *Tablettes votives bouddhiques du Siam,* in Etudes Asiatiques, BEFEO, Paris, 1925.)

TMB   Chand and Khien, *Thai Monumental Bronzes* (Bankok, 1957).

@ @

The Architecture and Sculpture of Siam

BY A. B. GRISWOLD

ᘓ ᘓ

The Buddha, going into trance, caused jets of flame to dart out
from his body. The whole land caught fire and the people were terrified.
As if removing a thorn from their flesh by means of another thorn,
he extinguished the flames of their passions by means of his own
miraculous flame. The people, thinking he must be the Sun-god
or the god of fire, fell down and worshipped him.

—Pūjāvaliya

Preliminary Note

IT IS A PLEASURE to record my gratitude to Prince Subhadradis Diskul and his associates at the National Museum in Bangkok, and equally to Luang Boribal Buribandh, now retired. If it had not been for their help I could not have written the following pages. My indebtedness to them, indeed, extends over a long period of years, during which they have always stood ready to aid my researches, though they have not always agreed with my conclusions.

Several decades ago, scholars tentatively divided the sculpture of Siam into a number of different groups on the basis of type and style, naming each group for the region where it was thought to have centered. In most cases the region that provided the name had at one time been the seat of a principality to which a certain amount of history could be attached. The names were intelligently chosen, and on the whole they are appropriate, though in the light of further research a few of them seem to me rather misleading.

The chief objection to them is that, having come into general use, they are liable to be taken too literally. The public have a tendency to confuse type and style together; and then, because of the names given the groups, to confuse both with *locality* and *period*. By this means a fictitious art history can be constructed; and if it is used to fill out the gaps in political history, there is no limit to what may happen. My friends at the National Museum are to be congratulated for resisting such fancies; and in order to put some restraint on the public fondness for them they have worked out the following scheme:

Dvāravatī style	6th – 11th century
Śrīvijaya style	8th – 13th century
Lopburî style	11th – 14th century
Chieng Sèn style	12th – 20th century
Sukhodaya style	13th – 15th century
Ŭ Tòng style	12th – 15th century
Ayudhyā style	15th to late 18th century
Bangkok style	Late 18th century to present

This is the scheme used by Prince Subhadradis in his Catalogue notes (pages 184-214). For the most part I use it too, but I have discarded the term *Chieng Sèn* in favor of the more general term *northern Siam,* and in some cases I have proposed a different dating. In the discussion of certain objects in the Exhibition, the reader will therefore find some discrepancies between my text and Prince Subhadradis's Catalogue.

I should perhaps add a word about spelling and nomenclature.

For Sanskrit and Pali words I have naturally used the standard transliteration. Many Siamese names are borrowed directly from those languages, with the spelling unaltered though the pronunciation may be quite different; and here too, for the convenience of readers who are acquainted with the Indian classical languages, I usually use the same transliteration. For words of Tai origin, on the other hand, this system is extremely awkward. For them (and also for certain names derived from Sanskrit where the connection is not strongly felt) I have adopted a simple phonetic scheme in which the consonants are to be pronounced as in English, and the vowels as in Italian (note that *è* and *ò* are the Italian "open" *e* and *o*; *é* and *ó,* the "closed;" in other cases a circumflex indicates a long vowel; *ü* and *ö* are approximately as in German; pronounce *g* as in *backgammon.*)

The reader may wonder why I persist in using the name *Siam,* since the country is today officially called *Thailand.* The latter is a translation of *Müang Tai* (or *Thai,* as it is often written, though in any case pronounced nearly like the English word "tie"). I am writing about the past, and to a considerable extent about the country before the Tai were settled there: to call it "the land of the Tai" would be needlessly confusing. Though the name *Siam* is admittedly an anachronism for the early period, long usage authorizes it as a purely geographical expression. As to *Tai* and *Siamese,* which are more or less interchangeable, it is sometimes convenient to make a distinction, using *Tai* for members of that race whatever country they were living in, and *Siamese* for citizens of Siam, no matter what their racial origin.

A. B. GRISWOLD

A Note on the Illustrations: Marginal figure references designate illustrations, which are grouped by period and style. Objects in the Exhibition which are not illustrated are referred to marginally by catalogue number. In the Catalogue proper (which begins on p. 184) a figure reference is given for each object illustrated.

1. Doctrines and Reminders

6 *Theravāda Buddhism* 9

THE LEADERS of the Theravāda, "the Doctrine of the Senior Monkhood," strive to safeguard the purity of the Buddha's teaching. The doctrine of rationalism was always in danger of being contaminated by the superstitions of its neighbors: since immemorial times a huge population of spirits have haunted India and Southeast Asia, demanding to be placated with offerings, or yielding to the coercion of spells. Spirits cause rain and drought, good crops or bad; disease and accidents, success or failure in love and gambling and warfare. They are not immortal; like all living beings they are subject to the law of transmigration. At death every creature is reborn as some other creature, whether god or demon, man or beast. The wheel of transmigration carries them all in an endless round; those at the top will in due course be plunged down to the bottom, and all are condemned for eternity to existence after existence in which delights are brief and misery long.

The monks long ago learned to live on peaceful terms with the spirits, putting them to use as figures of speech rather than trying to obliterate them. Tolerance is a cardinal principle of Buddhism; and to persecute the spirit-worshipers for their beliefs would be both unkind and impractical.

Instead, the monks aim to set an example of virtue and rational behavior, perfecting their own minds and educating others. Some specialize in studying the Pali texts and preaching the Doctrine. Some devote themselves to *meditation:* the exercise begins with breath-control; then it goes on to mental concentration, with or without the aid of fixing the gaze on a *device,* such as a patch of color, a spot of earth, a cup of water, the air in an empty bowl, or the flame of a lamp; then by progressive stages it proceeds to abstraction and trance.

Within the Theravāda there are two very different sorts of Buddhists – rationalists and pious believers.

To the rationalists the Doctrine is a philosophy that parallels modern scientific thought, and at the same time a moral code based on self-restraint and kindness. The Buddha was a man, not a god; and he proposed to abolish suffering, not by reference to any deity but by purely human means: he showed that the gods, if there are such beings, are no less subject to the law of impermanence than men and animals. There is nothing like a soul that can be reborn, though the consequences of every deed that is done go on forever. Craving, malice and delusion are the cause of present misery, and of its prolongation after death. Nirvana is their extinction, and a man who has attained it passes into *Final Nirvana* when he dies.

Pious believers, on the other hand, cannot help feeling that the Buddha is a kind of super-god who is accessible to prayer. For them transmigration is a reality to be taken literally; and so, like prudent people who make regular deposits in a saving bank, they lay up a store of *acts of merit* that will entitle them to specific rewards in future lives: so much for freeing a caged bird, so much for giving alms to a monk, so much for offering flowers to an image of the Buddha.

The Canon of the Theravādins, preserved in the Pali language, seems to authorize the views of both the rationalists and the pious believers. In many passages we see the Buddha as a skeptic, gently scornful of magic and superstition, rejecting the supernatural basis of religion though maintaining its moral values. In other passages we see him performing miracles, flying through the air, and teaching his disciples charms to tame demons.

The contradiction vanishes if passages of the first sort are taken as factual, and the second as metaphorical. They reflect different aspects of the same truth. Both were necessary if Buddhism was to become an active force for good among vast numbers of people. In addressing sophisticated listeners the Buddha used a terminology that was common to many Indian schools of philosophy, but gave it a new meaning. In talking to simple people he used familiar concepts as allegories, and homely anecdotes to point a moral. Sometimes the pious remembered the anecdote more distinctly than the moral, or mistook the allegory for the recital of a real event.

The passages that depict Indra and Brahmā as the Sage's loyal supporters are not pious frauds, nor are the passages that tell of godlings and demons being converted to the Doctrine. As the gods had no power except in the minds of those who believed in them, their conversion precisely signifies the conversion of their worshipers. New converts gave over to the Buddha their cairns and hilltops, their sacred groves and altars, transferring their ancient forms of veneration to him as they transferred their allegiance. Men who had made bloody sacrifices to earth-demons might offer flowers and incense to the Sage who induced the demons to renounce their evil life; the cult of serpents had a gentler meaning when the serpents were known as protectors of the Buddha; trees, long worshiped as the abode of dryads, were now honored as reminders of those particular trees under which he had meditated. Fire-worshipers who became Buddhists would see the Sage as a boundless flame, imitated by the monks as lesser lamps; they would think of him in terms of the solar myths, and honor him with the rite of circumambulation in the sunwise direction; and the most learned among them, having joined the order, would seek to visualize him by practicing meditation with a *fire device*.

The Buddha, when he knew his death was approaching, told his disciples that they must be "lamps unto themselves," taking the initiative and carrying on his work without him.

The rationalists among them could think for themselves, but it would be harder for the others, less strong-minded but not less devoted, who had relied on him to do their thinking for them. It would help if they could be allowed to perform some regular act of homage to the memory of the Sage in whom they had put their faith; and many converts, if they were denied a similar solace, would easily fall back into the superstitions from which he had rescued them. The Buddha therefore authorized the faithful to make pilgrimages to the scenes of the four Great Events of his career: Kapilavastu, where he was born; Bodhgayā, where he attained Enlightenment in the shelter of the Bo tree; Sarnāth, where he "set the wheel of the Doctrine in motion" by preaching the First Sermon; and Kuśinagara, where he now lay dying. When they visited these places they would visualize the Events connected with them, remember his victories over evil and ignorance, and so be inspired to imitate him. If that was not sufficient, they could gather his bodily relics, such as bones and teeth, after his cremation; they could build stupas, mounds of earth or masonry, to contain them; and the stupas, by reminding people of the Doctrine, would make their hearts calm and happy.

The sites of the Great Events were *reminders by association (paribhogacetiya)*; and so, more precisely, were the stupas containing relics, the stone altar-slabs on which he had sat to meditate or to preach, the Bo tree which sheltered him at the moment of Enlightenment, and the marks of his footsole imprinted on mountain-top or river-bank.

In the course of centuries the bodily relics were divided and sub-divided, but not as rapidly as the stupas multiplied in number. The great majority of stupas are *replicas* of stupas that contain relics, but contain none themselves. Such replicas are recognized as *indicative reminders (uddesikacetiya)* – objects, neutral in themselves, which the general opinion might regard as substitutes for reminders by association. Replicas of the scenes of the Great Events are also indicative reminders; and by the power of mental projection small clay tablets stamped with the figure of a Bo tree or a wheel enable people in distant places to make pilgrimages to Bodhgayā or Sarnāth without leaving home.

Stupas are not only reminders to Buddhists; in early days they must also have been powerful instruments for attracting converts. For that purpose their symbolism was so designed that it could be interpreted in various ways: it had to make sense to Buddhists and non-Buddhists alike. The stupa itself, a solid dome of masonry, or of earth faced with masonry, was often gilded or covered with gleaming tile, and set about with lamps at night. The round or square base that supported it tended to grow taller and turn into a cylinder, a cube, or a pyramid. To the top of the dome a little pavilion *(harmikā)* was added, and on top of that an honorific parasol of several tiers, often stylized into a tall spire ringed with mouldings, with a piece of crystal or other reflecting material at the very top to catch the light.

Monuments like this could hardly help recalling the altars of fire-worshipers; and memories of an even more ancient tradition clung to them. The Mesopotamians built ziggurats, pyramids reaching to heaven, magic mountains by which the earth, with its burden of perished ancestors, was bound to the empyrean. For the Chinese a similar magic kept order in the kingdom by relating it to the order of the universe. The Indians, too, sought to harmonize human activity with the order of the universe and with the stars in their courses. Such conceptions could turn the base of a stupa into an artificial mountain, a pyramid of several storeys, holding, like the ziggurat, a wealth of astrological data.

To Hindus and Buddhists alike, the pyramid recalls Meru, the central mountain of the Indian world. The pavilion on its summit is Indra's paradise of sensuous delights, while the tiers of the spire recall the heavens of Brahmā and even more abstract abodes of the blessed soaring far above in the atmosphere. The mast of the spire is the axis of the universe, marking its center, reaching deep down through the base of the stupa into the earth and the watery realm of the *nāgas* who are guardians of subterranean treasure. The same mast recalls the center of the Buddhist world, the Bo tree at Bodhgayā under whose branches the great Sage achieved Enlightenment. All sorts of creatures guard and support the stupa, dedicating to it the resources of their respective realms. Elephants may represent the earth; *makaras* and *nāgas*, aquatic monsters and serpent-spirits, the waters; *garudas,* divine birds, the air; lions, bulls and horses, or composites of all three, fire and the fiery sun; the symbolism suggests a rich variety of meanings to different beholders. The architecture emphasizes fire and water, the flame motif and the water-monster and the serpent, sun, lightning and rain, together with an animated profusion of vegetation, the wealth of a well-watered agriculture and the delight of converts from the old tree-cults.

Educated opinion in India long held the notion of image-making in contempt; images were a concession to the ignorant who could not grapple with sublime abstractions. In the early bas-reliefs depicting scenes from his life, the Buddha himself is invisible. His presence is made known by an *aniconic* symbol: a pair of footprints, a stone altar-slab, a tree or a pillar of fire, a wheel, a parasol. The symbols were not invented; they were already in men's minds. To converts from the older cults of earth, stones, trees, fire and sun, they would be the best reminders of the Sage, the best means to worship him, and the best devices for meditation and trance.

Added together in ascending order, the symbols formed a coherent whole, a scheme for visualizing the Buddha, a kind of armature for an imaginary statue which could be seen only by means of meditation. The footprints became feet, the tree or pillar of fire became the trunk of the body, the disk became the halo behind the head. The Sage was more and more distinctly perceived, seated on the slab or standing, and shaded by the honorific parasol.

When at length sculpture began to portray the Buddha in human form, the earlier symbols still constituted, as it were, the armature inside the statue: like the symbols, the statue is an *indicative reminder*. The symbols owe their power to the fact that they are replicas of *reminders by association;* by the same reasoning, the statue must be a replica – but of what? The Canon mentions no reminder by association that could possibly furnish the complete model; but legend supplies the omission by relating that certain likenesses of the Sage were made during his lifetime by persons who knew his appearance well. To the faithful in the Gupta period, more than eight centuries after his death, such images were genuine reminders by association. The fact that they no longer existed or, to speak bluntly, never had existed, was no obstacle; there were plenty of reputed replicas of them, made by an earlier generation at Gandhāra and Mathurā, and these would serve well enough as models for further replicas.

In Indian art a replica is not necessarily an exact copy. Tradition discountenanced working in the presence of a model. An artist who wanted to paint a tree, for instance, was supposed to study it, for months on end if necessary, until he knew it thoroughly, and then go away and do his work from memory. He was to paint not what was before his eyes, but what his mind knew. When a sculptor wished to carve an image of the Buddha, it would certainly not occur to him to have a human being pose for it. His model would be an earlier statue; and if he was a first-rate artist he would study and worship it simultaneously by means of the meditational technique, until it was so firmly fixed in his mind that there would be no need to look at it again after he took up his chisel. Whenever a serious work of art was to be executed, the qualities of the model were transmitted to it indirectly, by means of a *memory-picture*.

Gupta art thus sets a standard of beauty above and beyond the ordinary senses. The Buddha is a Yogi suffused with fiery energy, the embodiment of a flame. His *supernatural anatomy* gives fresh meaning to Yogic concepts of physical development, and to auspicious marks by which diviners could read the whole body as a palmist reads the hand. A rounded excrescence, the *ushṇīsha*, crowns the skull; the ear-lobes are elongated; the curls of hair turn in the sunwise direction. There is no display of muscles, veins or bony articulation. A sun-disk is the Buddha's halo, and when the same sign reappears in miniature on his forehead, like a sect-mark painted on the brow of a sun-worshiper, it is thought of as a tuft of hair emitting luminous rays. Gilding the image confirms its luminous significance; and the wheel on palm and footsole, while it symbolizes the onward progress of the Doctrine, still recalls the sun's power.

The monastic robe – in reality a large oblong sheet, worn like a toga – becomes a mere diagram. The incandescence of the Sage's body shines through it and reduces it to transparency; like a thin handkerchief thrown over an electric bulb, the fabric vanishes, leaving only a few hems where it lies on the body, and a pattern of folds where it falls free.

The cult image is a cut-out from one or another of the standard bas-reliefs depicting episodes from the sacred legend. The prince who is destined to become Buddha has been roused by a four-fold vision of pain and release; he has set out to discover the cause of suffering and how it can be abolished; he has become a wandering ascetic, and submitted to dreadful austerities that proved useless. He finally solves the problem by *meditation;* and so sculpture often shows him, sitting cross-legged with his hands in his lap, in the classic posture of Yogic trance. At Bodhga-yā, on the eve of Enlightenment, he is tempted like Saint Anthony with a succession of distracting visions both alluring and horrible; he disperses them by moving his right hand from the meditative position to his knee, pointing downward to *call the Earth to witness (bhūmisparśa)* and testify his worthiness to *triumph over evil (māravijaya)*. This gesture represents the Enlightenment; and like a stage property in a play, a Bo tree may be added to identify the scene. He spends the next seven weeks nearby, elaborating his Doctrine from the basic truths he has learned in meditation. Presently he journeys to the Deer Park at Sarnāth and preaches the First Sermon: sitting with his hands held in front of his chest, thumb and forefinger joined, he *sets in motion the wheel of the Doctrine* in a landscape identified by a pair of deer with a wheel between them. The same gesture serves for the *great magical display* by which the heretics are confounded. Besides the seated posture there are three other permissible attitudes. The sculptured Sage stands or walks when *taming the enraged elephant* that a jealous rival turns loose against him, or when *descending from heaven* on a miraculous ladder after preaching for three months to his mother and a concourse of gods. He accompanies his action with one of those vivid gestures that are so useful among a polyglot people: when *dispelling fear* his right hand is raised, with the fingers pointing up; when *bestowing favors* his right hand is lowered, with the palm facing forward and the fingers pointing down. At the end of a long life, he lies on his right side with his head resting on his hand and *passes into final Nirvana.*

⑥ *Hinduism and Buddhism* ⑨

IN THE GUPTA PERIOD the ancient gods, so long eclipsed by Buddhism, took on fresh life. Everything contributed; a literary renaissance, with its wistful retrospect of the Vedic age; drama and religious dance; piety and superstition, grossly manifested at the village level, but welded somehow with more sublime conceptions by the Brahmins into an extremely subtle philosophy.

Hinduism offered worshipers a wide selection. Vishṇu, Siva and the other gods, together with their consorts or female counterparts, absorbed the powers of many a totemic animal, *genius loci,* and figure of heroic legend. They were abstract principles as well: creation and destruction, frightfulness and mercy, sensuality and asceticism, havoc and peace. With their violent extremes, their imperious claims and their tender favoritisms, deities of this sort might well attract anyone who found Buddhism too austere and cold. Demanding to be worshiped, they trampled down their enemies, tore their victims limb from limb, rode in triumph on their chosen beasts, reassured their devotees with a gesture.

They appear thus in sculpture, sometimes with many heads, like dancers in one posture after another painted in *futurismo,* or with many hands, like jugglers brandishing in succession the instruments of magic, sword, club, noose, flame, book, shell, and so on. Such objects were thought of as attributes of the absolute, the sword as power, the book as knowledge, the shell as eloquence. Painted blue, green, red or white, the image took on the identity of the divinity of corresponding hue, who could also be conjured up by the worshiper in trance from a device consisting of a patch of that color.

Buddhism split into numerous sects, which grouped themselves into two great divisions.

In northern India, the organizers of the *Mahāyāna,* the Greater Vehicle, introduced a wealth of new doctrine. Using the Sanskrit language, adopting a good deal of Brahmanical philosophy and ritual, they made mysticism paramount. The Buddha was no longer merely the Sage of historical legend; his qualities proliferated innumerable Buddhas in time, space and the dimensions of speculation. Images of these Buddhas, derived by selection from images of the historical Buddha, were distinguished from one another chiefly by the gestures they performed. Images of the Buddha *wearing the attire of royalty* were copies of earlier statues in monastic dress, reproducing in stone the real gems and silks that the faithful presented them. The ideal of unselfishness was represented by the Bodhisattvas who, when on the point of achieving Nirvana, voluntarily postponed its accomplishment until all creatures should be delivered: when addressed in prayer, they stood ready to come to mankind's assistance. Seen in sculpture they looked like their counterparts of the Hindu pantheon, but with a small clue to the difference, such as the little Buddha image in the headdress of Avalokiteśvara (Lokeśvara) that sets him apart from Śiva.

Tantric magical science possessed itself of a section of the *Mahāyāna:* for a time the *Vajrayāna,* or Adamantine Vehicle, and its counterpart in Hinduism, sought the same empyrean by the same techniques.

As to the Doctrine the Buddha himself had preached – disparagingly called *Hīnayāna,* the Lesser Vehicle, by the exponents of the Greater – its chief adherents were the Theravādins who clung to the Pali Canon in South India and Ceylon.

The various Indian religions, living together peaceably enough, borrowed architectural inventions freely from one another. In some Buddhist monasteries the monks lived in huge wooden mountains, hollow pyramids of many storeys; each storey held rows of cells whose rounded openings, giving access to the terraces, suggested cave-mouths; the terraces, guarded by a company of mythical creatures, bristled with a profusion of little stupas, the lesser peaks of the central mountain.

When shrines were needed, these wooden structures could be copied in masonry. The terraces multiplied in number but became less distinct. The two lower storeys constituted the sanctuary, while the superstructure became a tall crowning obelisk covered with a pattern in bas-relief of many horizontal shelves and false-dormers *(kūḍu)*. Something like this design appears at Bodhgayā: the Mahābodhi is a large square base supporting a massive obelisk, with lesser obelisks at the corners.

With the revival of Brahminism, the Hindus interpreted the wooden pyramid in stone in their own way. Along the terraces the false-dormers remained and the auspicious animals multiplied, while the stupas were changed to little stone buildings that reproduced the leafy huts of fire-worshipers and the airy pavilions of celestials. The obelisk might take on a convex outline (the Hindu *śikhara),* and a stone forechamber with a terraced roof might be attached to one side of it.

Secular architecture contributed its splendors to religion. Wooden palaces, with their roofs shaped like tunnel-vaults, were copied in the living rock at Ajanta, Ellora, and elsewhere: the cave-temples were presents from royalty who wished to furnish the austere grottoes of holy men with the elegance of their own abodes. The same abodes in miniature provided the design for the aerial palaces on Hindu temple-roofs, and their rounded gables inspired the form of niches and false-dormers.

Pyramids and obelisks, stupa-bases and temples and temple roofs, all recall the artificial mountain. Bristling with lesser peaks, pierced with cave-mouths, guarded by sprites and chimeras, these replicas of Meru transfer the center of the universe to any point where men's minds require it.

⑥ *Stupa-building in Siam* ⑨

IN EARLY DAYS when Buddhist monks were carrying the Doctrine from India and Ceylon to the peoples of Southeast Asia, it was the custom to announce their arrival in a town by building a stupa. The first converts might be still too few to afford a very imposing monument; but no matter how small and plain it might be, it would always be remembered with special veneration as the first one built there.

In the course of time the pious would wish to have a more splendid memorial on the same exact spot; but as they would not think of demolishing so sacred an object, they would build a larger stupa *encasing* the old one. Some monuments have three or more successive encasements, raising them from an original height of a few yards to the size of Saint Paul's Cathedral.

A person who builds a stupa does not invent a new form. Whether he is encasing or building afresh, he copies an old one: such is the rule for indicative reminders. But the copy need not be very exact, and indeed it cannot be if the scale is drastically changed: if it is much reduced, as when a monument is copied in miniature, details will be omitted; if it is enlarged, as when a miniature model is copied in monumental dimensions, the details may be magnified, but that is only feasible up to a certain point, and beyond it the alternative is to multiply them.

⑥ *Buddha images in Siam* ⑨

A BUDDHA IMAGE has to perform two quite different functions, depending on the needs of the beholder: rationalists need only a reminder; pious believers want supernatural protection. It can best fulfill both needs if it has been designed without reference to the usual ideals of human beauty or the facts of anatomy. The composition should hold together not by any perceptible articulation, but by its internal armature of old aniconic symbols.

The image-maker had no desire to be original: he was always a copyist. It may be hard for us to believe that the masterpieces are all copies, no less than the stereotyped statuettes produced by the thousand for the general market; to us in the West the difference between a genuine old master and a copy is immeasurable, even if we have to get an expert to decide which it is. In the art of the image-maker, on the contrary, copying is not only the line of least resistance, it is (or was, until Western ideas began to break the tradition) a necessity: an indicative reminder is, by definition, a copy.

When the patron who commissioned an image was a rationalist, he wanted the comprehensible and undisturbing symbolism that was already familiar; and if he happened to be sensitive to beauty he chose a model that gave him aesthetic satisfaction as conveying more perfectly the Sage's qualities. On the other hand, when the patron wanted a talisman that would inherit some fraction of the Buddha's infinite power, he would seek to assure its legitimacy in the line of descent from one of the legendary authentic likenesses; and so he would choose as a model some statue that had already proved itself by displaying unusual magical qualities. The chronicles of famous images, compiled in northern Siam, relate with pious satisfaction the miracles these reminders performed, and tell us how princes used all sorts of unscrupulous means to get them from their rivals. The chronicles often add that the loser begged to keep the image just a little while longer so as to have a copy made. They hint that when the request was granted it was the winner who got the copy, though he was none the wiser for it. Curiously enough, we are told, the princes who insisted most on getting the original often had difficulty in distinguishing it from others in the same image-house. Plainly they would be even less able to detect a copy that was endowed with almost the same magical powers. The replica would not have to be very precise in order to deceive such untrained eyes; but it would have to reproduce certain features in order to perform miracles.

Like the second edition of a book, the copy had to *be* like the original, not necessarily to *look* like it. The content, the iconography, was essential; the format, the sculptural style, was arbitrary or optional. When the sculptor was talented, and the patron discriminating, the copy might well surpass the original in beauty.

☾ *Clues to chronology* ☽

THE CHRONOLOGY of sculpture in Siam is full of unsolved problems. In an art that consists principally of Buddha images, an art that copies endlessly but by no means precisely, the interpretation of the data is singularly difficult. Those images that have dated inscriptions on their pedestals are of course our best guides, but there are unfortunately very few of them. For nearly all the rest the only clues to age are iconography and style.

The *iconography* of a Buddha image means three things: anatomy, dress, posture. The sculpture of Siam, in the main, deviates little from the ideals established by Indian art in all three. Indeed there is not much latitude for choice. The *anatomy* may vary, within limits, as to the canons of proportion and the form of the supernatural details. The *dress* is usually the monk's garb, covering either both shoulders or the left shoulder only; occasionally it is a princely garment; in either case it is very stylized. Four *postures* are permissible: walking, standing, sitting, reclining; there are less than a dozen usual *gestures* of the hand.

That is just about all the iconography an image-maker who serves the Theravāda needs. Unlike those who portray the Hindu gods, he has no use for a multiplication of heads and arms, no use for postures charged with emotion, no use for significant attributes held in the hands, and very little use for smart dress and jewels. The iconography of a Buddha image systematically excludes everything that might be subject to changing fashions, and consequently everything that might furnish us the most helpful clues to chronology.

Style depends on another order of ideas. How does the artist relate masses and planes? Does he give his figure a solid three-dimensional quality or does he think more in terms of bas-relief? What patterns of line and silhouette does he make use of? What rhythm and movement does he impart? What convention does he adopt to represent clothing? What is the facial expression? Do the features recall some particular race or nationality, or even an individual, or are they generalized and ideal?

In matters of this sort, which we might hope would provide reliable clues, the image-maker depended on the training he had received in early youth. Even the most inspired artist seldom had any reason to depart from it; while the ordinary craftsman who turned out cheap bronze statuettes for the general market mechanically reproduced the old formulas, saving himself trouble, if he wished, by using soapstone dies to stamp in the clay and wax such repetitive details as curls, ears, hands, and the lotus decoration of a pedestal.

Such an art might be expected to follow a slow and orderly evolution. Indeed it might have done so if all the sculptors copied as faithfully as they could, and if the model the patron chose was always a product of their own school. But if he chose a model of a sort the sculptor had never seen before – a little figure imported from some distant holy place, or an antique reputed to be nearer in the line of descent to one of the originals – the evolution could be suddenly broken.

A moment's reflection will show that iconography travels from one place to another when an image makes the trip and inspires a copy; and it leaps from the past to the present when an ancient image is exhumed and copied. Style is less adventurous, traveling for the most part only when artists travel. Yet iconography and style cannot be wholly dissociated; and the copyist may reproduce one or two of the most striking stylistic features of the unfamiliar model, though he would certainly make no attempt to reproduce its style as a whole.

The copying of alien or antique works forces the sculptor, no matter how reluctantly, to summon up his latent powers of invention. If the model is small and the copy is to be life-size, he will have to improvise extensive passages. If it is a bas-relief and the copy is to be in the full round, he will have to improvise a third dimension and a back. He will base the improvisation on his own training and his recollections of other images, adjusting them to whatever he can discern in the model.

When this sort of thing happens, an *aberrant type* is produced. If there are only one or two examples of it, it will probably escape our notice altogether. But if it happens to serve as a model for a fresh series, a *new style* may come into being.

2. Dvāravatī and its Neighbors

INDIAN MERCHANTS had been trading with Southeast Asia since immemorial times. Some of them settled there and married into the families of local chieftains; so trading-posts grew into principalities, which bound themselves to one another in shifting patterns of vassalage. Buddhist monks were zealous in spreading the Doctrine, while learned Brahmins introduced the Hindu religions, as well as the sciences, arts and techniques of India. One of the earliest of the Indianizing kingdoms was Fu-nan, founded in the first century A. D. It survived for over 500 years, for a time dominating the greater part of Cambodia and Siam.

One of its successor states was Dvāravatī, whose chief cities lay within a 100-mile radius of modern Bangkok. The Tai were not yet settled in Siam; the ruling classes of Dvāravatī were Mòn, and the kingdom was a member of a Mòn confederation that reached westward to Thaton. At the beginning of the 11th century Dvāravatī was annexed to the Khmer Empire: and not long afterwards the Burmese under King Aniruddha conquered the western Mòn. But the little Mòn kingdom of Haripuñjaya (Lampûn), an offshoot of Dvāravatī in northern Siam, managed to remain independent until the closing years of the 13th century.

A great number of antiquities, almost all of them associated with Theravāda Buddhism, are attributed to the *Dvāravatī style,* though not necessarily to regions that were part of the kingdom nor to the period of its independence. They are usually dated between the 6th and the 11th century, but if we include the Mòn style of Lampûn we must extend it to the end of the 13th.

Architecture

NOTHING SURVIVES of Dvāravatī architecture except foundations and fragments in the region where the kingdom centered, and one or two monuments at Lampûn. Foundations were made of laterite, which when freshly dug is soft and clay-like; it can easily be cut into blocks or slabs, and gradually hardens to a stone-like consistency when exposed to the air. Brick was the principal material used for monuments. The bricks, which were much larger than in modern times, were fitted together with care, laid without mortar, and bound with some sort of vegetable glue.

Architectural trim was sometimes of carved stone, but more generally of stucco, a mixture of sand and lime with a binding of glue, often with a terra cotta armature inside.

One type of stupa, which is known from a small stone model, preserves an archaic Indian tradition. *fig. 1 a*

A second type, known from a larger stone model and from several bas-reliefs, has a pot-shaped dome recalling the vase of plenty *(puṇṇaghata)*. On top is a mast ringed with disks of diminishing circumference, the multi-tiered parasol. Its finial is a bulb, which doubtless represents – though the reliefs magnify its size out of all proportion to reality – a piece of crystal or some other reflecting material. *figs. 1 b, c, .d, e and f*

A third type, which is far more elaborate, can be seen at Wat Kūkuṭa, near Lampûn. It assumed its present form in 1218 when it was rebuilt after an earthquake. It is a slender pyramid of five storeys; the top, which must have included the stupa proper and a spire, is broken off. Sixty niches contain terra cotta Buddha images, three on each face of each storey; and four of the five storeys have miniature stupas at the corners. As the eye travels upward the storeys decrease in height, with their niches and images and stupas diminishing in proportion. A happy optical illusion results, which increases the apparent height of the monument. *fig. 2*

We can guess at the vanished splendors of Dvāravatī architecture by glancing at the structures built by Mòn architects for their Burmese conquerors at Pagán in the late 11th and early 12th centuries: those vast stupas and shrines must have had their prototypes in a Mòn tradition shared by Dvāravatī. If so, the shrines were of two main types.

The first evolves from a stupa whose base is a high cube of solid masonry with a niche on each face for a cult image. By enclosing the cube in a quadrangular corridor roofed with a brick vault, the structure is converted into a shrine. But it is an odd sort of shrine, as most of the interior is blocked by the great cube of masonry that carries the stupa. The remains excavated in 1939-40 at Wat Braḥ Meru, Nagara Paṭhama, appear to have belonged to a structure of this sort, though all but the lower portions had crumbled into a chaotic heap of rubble. *fig. 3 a*

The other type of shrine at Pagán is an adaptation of the Hindu temple to Buddhist uses. It is a square brick building with latticed windows on three sides and an entrance on the fourth, often preceded by a forechamber. No central block of masonry obstructs the interior; if necessary, there are piers to help support the weight of the pyramidal roof. Excavations at one or two Dvāravatī sites have disclosed square platforms which were doubtless bases for structures of this sort. *fig. 3 b*

The assembly-halls *(vihāra)* of monasteries were presumably of wood or brick. The remains of one rather elaborate example have been excavated, which recall the remains of assembly-halls discovered at Anurādhapura in Ceylon. The high oblong platform, with projecting bays and re-entrant angles, is faced with laterite blocks carved into a series of mouldings. On the platform were found fragments of the round laterite columns that supported the roof, presumably of tile.

fig. 5   Our Exhibition contains a fascinating fragment of architectural stone-work from Nagara Paṭhama, probably dating from the 7th or 8th century. It is part of a larger fragment, the rest of which is at the National Museum in Bangkok. Seen from below, the under-surface is carved in a floral motif which forms a kind of frame around a large rectangular hole. At first glance it is disconcerting to find carving on a part that would normally be hidden; but here, I believe, is a clue to its function. The hole must have accommodated a tall stone shaft which raised the structure high into the air, doubtless on the terrace of a stupa base or the roof of a shrine, where the frame could, after all, be seen from below. The composition, with its godlings peering out through the false-dormers, is an aerial palace.

❧ Sculpture ☙

THE DVARAVATI SCULPTORS owed much to Indian example, and especially to the late Gupta art of the cave-temples. But they did not take over the conventions of any one Indian school wholesale: their work shows a mixed heritage, which can best be explained if it is admitted that a school of art under other auspices had been flourishing in the locality before the earliest surviving Dvāravatī works were *fig. 7*   made. Some of these, indeed, which appear to date from the late 6th century, show a mastery of technique that could hardly have been achieved overnight; yet they are too far removed from their Indian counterparts to have been made by Indian artists, either in India or in Siam.

Stone statues of the Buddha: standing figures. If we look at a large number of Dvāravatī stone statues in the standing position, we shall see at once how little the iconography varies. Apart from two or three aberrant images, which we can dismiss from consideration, there are only two types.

Before studying them, let us glance at some of their predecessors. In Gupta art the standing Buddha may wear the robe either in the *covered* scheme, draped over both shoulders, or in the *open* scheme, leaving the right shoulder bare. The right hand may be held upward, *dispelling fear;* or it may be held down, *bestowing favors.* The left hand, whether held downward or at shoulder-level, always grasps a flap of the robe. Theoretically eight different types are available, by combining either scheme of the robe with any of the four gesture patterns: both hands up;

both down; right up and left down; right down and left up. Most of these can be counted in the little reliefs depicting scenes from the Buddha's life; but for separate images the choice narrows: the north Indian Gupta has only two types, and the late Gupta of the cave-temples has only three. Each of these schools has its own *standard* type, for which it has an overwhelming preference; in addition, north India has one *occasional* type, and the cave-temples have two. The cave-temples ignore the north Indian standard type, basing *their* standard on the north Indian occasional type. In like manner, Dvāravatī ignores both the north Indian and the cave-temple standard, adopting one of the cave-temple occasional types for *its* occasional, and the other for its standard.

While the information in the following table may not appear very significant, it really provides the key to Siamese iconography.

Late Gupta (cave-temples)	Robe	Right hand	Left hand	
1. Standard	open	down (gesture)	up (holding robe)	*fig. 74*
2. Occasional	covered	down (gesture)	up (holding robe)	*fig. 10*
3. Occasional	covered	up (gesture)	up (holding robe)	*fig. 8*
Dvāravatī				
4. Standard	covered	up (gesture)	up (gesture)	*figs. 9, 12*
5. Occasional	covered	down (gesture)	up (holding robe)	*fig. 11*

The Dvāravatī occasional type (no. 5) need not detain us long. It faithfully preserves the iconography of its Indian counterpart (no. 2). Archeologists usually take such fidelity to be a sign of relatively early date; but in this case its meaning remains to be tested.

The Dvāravatī *standard* type merits a longer examination. To illustrate it, let us take the finest surviving example, a statue made of the grey or greyish-blue limestone that most often provided the material for sculpture. Though it is not an exact copy of any Indian statue I know of, it is obviously related to one of the cave-temple types (no. 3). Judging from the style of writing that appears in a short inscription on the base, it dates from the 7th century. There is a similar statue in our Exhibition, and also a stone head of the same sort. Both, I take it, are early pieces, not far removed in date from the statue I am about to describe. The supernatural anatomy is like the Gupta. The robe, worn in the covered scheme, is stylized further in the interest of symmetry; but though it is not naturalistically rendered, its outline is easily intelligible to anyone acquainted with the real monastic dress. The posture is almost the same as in the Indian model, but the hands were doing something else: judging from other statues of the same type, they were both performing the gesture

fig. 9

figs. 12 and 7

cf. fig. 22

of *exposition (vitarka),* which is like *dispelling fear* except that the thumb and fore-finger are joined.

The modeling in general follows the Gupta idiom. The facial features are clearly delineated; an outline in delicate relief accents the silhouette of the lips; and the eyebrows join above the nose.

We might suppose that a Mòn artist, trained in a school that had once had Indian masters, carved this statue from a small and rather worn replica of the original, improvising where necessary to fill out the obscure details and enlarge the scale. But it may be a secondary or tertiary copy, through the intermediary of an earlier Mòn image, now vanished, in which the required improvisations had taken form. In any case a memory-picture, or perhaps several, intervened between the prototype and this statue. That is why the artist sees both dress and hand-position as more symmetrical, and the face as a generalized portrait of the most revered monks he knew in daily life. The face, indeed, recalls the Mòn physiognomy more than the Indian; yet the artist may also have heard of the Sanskrit list of 80 minor marks of the Buddha's person, which includes eyebrows joining together over the bridge of the nose.

The most striking difference between the Dvāravatī standard type and its Indian ancestor is in the function of the hands. The gesture of *exposition* is the right half, so to speak, of the *wheel-turning* gesture of seated figures. Standing figures in Gupta sculpture never perform it, and they never perform any gesture whatever with both hands, for the left is always occupied with grasping a corner of the robe. If the Dvāravatī standard type arose from copying an eroded replica of an Indian statue (number 3 in the Table), we may guess that its hands were too much damaged for the copyist to discern exactly what they were doing. It might be clear enough that they were raised to shoulder-level and that the palms faced forward; and the remnants of the left hand might show that the forefinger was bent. The most natural way for the copyist to interpret his data would be to suppose that both hands were doing what the right hand does in a seated *wheel-turning* figure.

This explanation may sound far-fetched, but I have seen plenty of instances in modern Siam when an old image needed to be repaired and the sculptor adopted a less thoughtful reconstruction.

At some point the new arrangement was given a new meaning. Since the 19th century at least, and perhaps far earlier, the gesture of *exposition,* performed with both hands, has been understood to signify the *descent from heaven.* It is generally believed that in Dvāravatī art it had the same significance; but that is by no means certain in all cases. Pagán, which inherited the Mòn iconography, uses something very much like it for three other episodes *(throwing the hairlock to heaven, ap-*

proaching the Bo tree, and *converting the yaksha Alavika).* For the *descent from heaven,* on the contrary, Pagán uses an adaptation of the late Gupta standard type (no. 1), with the robe in the open scheme, the right hand down (either performing a gesture or at rest), and the left hand up (touching the robe).

Stone statues of the Buddha: seated figures. Probably the most impressive single example of Dvāravatī art is the colossal Buddha seated in the "European manner" now in a chapel at the Braḥ Paṭhama monastery. Unlike most Dvāravatī statuary, it is carved in a whitish quartzite, which is now partly covered with lacquer and gilding. It is one of the four statues originally placed around the central cube of masonry in the Braḥ Meru monument. It is obviously based on a model in one of the cave-temples, but the hand-position is modified, this time by no means in the interest of symmetry. In the prototype the Buddha uses both hands to *turn the wheel of the Doctrine,* and in addition holds a flap of the robe in the left hand. Here the left hand does nothing; the right hand alone performs the gesture of *exposition* which is, as we have said, one-half of the wheel-turning gesture. We might suspect that the type originated when a Mòn sculptor copied a Gupta prototype through the intermediary of a replica whose left arm was broken off, and in improvising a new one he placed the hand at ease on the thigh.

When the Buddha sits with legs folded in the "Indian manner" Dvāravatī art has three possible arrangements: the *adamantine pose (vajrāsana),* the legs crossed, with each foot resting on the opposite thigh, the soles upward, as in Gupta art; the *hero pose (vīrāsana),* the legs folded with one simply lying on top of the other, as in Ceylon; and a variation of the latter, characteristic of Amarāvatī, with the legs merely crossed at the ankles. The last is the most frequent, even when the figure is in other respects drawn from the late Gupta. Such interpretations, based more on the sculptor's training than on the model itself, confirm the impression that a pre-Dvāravatī school had flourished locally under Amarāvatī inspiration.

Another recollection of Amarāvatī or Ceylon is preserved in the Dvāravatī figures of the Buddha seated on the coils of the *nāga* king.

Miscellaneous stone sculpture. Bas-reliefs of episodes from the Buddha's life must once have been numerous, but only a few survive. A pleasant example in the Sudarśana Monastery, Bangkok, unfortunately somewhat obscured by a heavy coating of gilt, appears to date from around the 7th or 8th century. It may be compared with some paintings of the same subject at Ajanta; if it was not directly inspired by them, it certainly springs from the same prototype. In the lower register, which depicts the *great magical display,* the Buddha sits in the center, flanked by the gods Indra and Brahmā holding fly-whisks. His footstool is a large lotus, held in the

fig. 13

fig. 14

fig. 15

fig. 16

fig. 16 and cat. no. 11

fig. 17

hands of a *nāga* of human form but with a seven-headed serpent's hood, who is supposed to be deep in the subterranean regions supporting the lotus-stem which is the axis of the world. Below the Buddha's throne, on one side are the princes who have come to applaud the miracle, and on the other side the discomfited heretics – naked ascetics and ascetics with matted hair – who are unable to match the Buddha's magic. Above are gods, their palms pressed together in worship of the Sage. Behind the throne is the miraculously-created mango tree, its branches supporting apparitions of the Buddha in various attitudes, performing a gesture with his right hand or his left as symmetry may require, and in one case, symmetry having triumphed over orthodoxy, reclining on his left side. In the upper register the Sage sits enthroned in heaven, again loyally attended by Indra and Brahmā with their flywhisks. At the foot of the throne, on the Buddha's right, sits his mother – clearly still female, although the texts says she was reborn as a male divinity; and all around and about, the other gods from the various heavens listen as he preaches the Metaphysics to her.

There are fifteen or twenty stone reliefs of a peculiar kind, in which a *garuda* supports a figure of the Buddha flanked by Indra and Brahmā. Sometimes, as in a relief discovered at Müang Braḥ Ratha, the two gods are absent; here the flames springing from the oval frame represent the Sage's fiery energy *(teja)*. In most of them the Buddha stands, performing the gesture of *exposition* with both hands. These compositions are generally said to represent the *descent from heaven,* and it may be true in most cases, but certainly not all, for sometimes the Buddha is seated. If most of the elements composing these reliefs have their counterparts in the Indian cave-temples, they are assembled in an original way whose significance eludes us.

fig. 18

A dozen or more stone *wheels of the Doctrine* have been unearthed at Nagara Paṭhama, and a few elsewhere. They recall the aniconic symbols of Aśokan art, but are separated from them by a thousand years or more: judging from the floral motifs carved on them, they mostly date from the 7th and 8th century, while one has a long inscription in Pali in letters attributable to the 9th. Associated with several of them is a deer, or a pair of deer, carved separately, to identify the site of the First Sermon. Sometimes a little divinity is attached to the wheel; when it is Sūrya, carrying a pair of lotuses, it is because the wheel was a solar symbol before the Buddhists adopted it, and the sun-god still clings to it.

fig. 20

Bronze Buddha images. Like the rest of the Indianized world, Dvāravatī used the *cire perdue* technique. The figure was first modeled in wax, or in wax over a clay core; then it was embedded in a mass of clay to make the mould; the mould, with the figure inside it, was baked, changing the clay to terra cotta and letting the wax run out; molten metal was poured in to take the place of the wax; finally, after a cooling-off period, the mould was broken away and the image given its finishing touches. The terra cotta core, if there was one, was left inside the image to reinforce it; but most Dvāravatī bronzes are small statuettes, made of solid metal without a core, the original figure having been made wholly of wax instead of wax over clay. They contain an unusually high proportion of metals other than copper and tin, and after long exposure in certain conditions they take on a thick and crusty patina.

fig. 24

Dvāravatī bronzes have been found all over Siam, but as they can so easily be carried about that means very little. They are impossible to date with any certainty, though they give the impression that they started later than the stone statuary, and continued longer.

The great majority of standing figures in bronze echo the standard type in stone. A few echo the occasional type. In other cases, particularly figures that wear the robe in the open scheme, it would be difficult to find a stone counterpart except in bas-relief. The bronzes that sit in the European fashion are almost certainly copies of the Braḥ Meru colossi, which must have been famous enough to inspire a good deal of copying.

fig. 22
fig. 23

fig. 21

Stucco. While the main image worshiped in a shrine would be made of stone, the niches of stupas bases often contained Buddha images of stucco. Stucco might be used for the heads of godlings that peer out through false-dormers, and for all sorts of architectural detail – balustrades and finials, real and mythical animals, guardian figures and lucky tokens. It also provided a less laborious technique than stone for making bas-reliefs of episodes from the Buddha's life. The scene was sketched in wet plaster on a brick wall; heads and sometimes bodies, previously modeled separately in stucco on an armature of terra cotta, were fixed on at the proper places; the rest of the scene was modeled in the wet plaster *in situ*. Not a single composition of this sort survives intact; they were shattered when the brick walls bearing them fell in ruins. The heads are tougher, and a good number have been recovered at the sites of ancient monuments. Many of them belonged to subsidiary personages in scenes from the Buddha's life, though it is seldom easy to identify them. We might guess that some are Brahmin teachers; another, a sprite; others are obviously demons. Occasionally a body is preserved: one of them, which perhaps belonged to Indra, is surely one of the most beautiful examples of Dvāravatī art known to us. In such stucco work the Mòn sculptor, held down by the bonds of orthodoxy when making Buddha images, gave free play to his delightful imagination.

figs. 26, 28

fig. 30

fig. 15

Votive tablets and terra cottas. A lead votive tablet in the Exhibition, which bears an inscription in *nāgarī* letters of the 9th or 10th century, depicts the famous Buddha image known as the *Lion of the Śākyas* in the Mahābodhi shrine at Bodhgayā. The statue appears to sit in a doorway, though it is supposed to be inside the shrine; the top of the obelisk, much reduced in size, seems to spring from the top of the niche, though in reality there is a huge mass of masonry between; and the surrounding stupas seem to float in the air, though they are really in the temple precinct. This sort of *explanatory perspective* records not what the eye sees but what the mind knows is there.

fig. 25

One of the most exquisite objects in the National Museum is a small terra cotta head from Nagara Paṭhama. Doubtless it belonged to a Buddha image that stood in a niche in the base of a stupa. The building, which has now completely disappeared, may have been something like Wat Kūkuṭa, where, as we have seen, the Buddha images in the niches are of terra cotta. In the Exhibition there is a small head from the latter monument.

fig. 19
fig. 29

fig. 27

The little terra cottas *en ronde bosse,* apparently produced from moulds, are a fascinating puzzle. I wonder if they are not *jātaka* figures.

☙ *Brahmanical sculpture of Dvāravatī and neighboring regions* ☙

As to the early relics of Hinduism in Siam, their relationship to Dvāravatī is not clear. We have several examples in our Exhibition. A detached hand comes from Rājapurī, where Buddhist antiquities of Dvāravatī style have also been discovered. A statue of Vishnu comes from farther down the Malay Peninsula. The finest piece comes from Śrī Deb, in northern central Siam, which was almost certainly not part of Dvāravatī. Dating from the 9th century or earlier, it is conceived and executed in the full round; and clearly the sculptor, though it is scarcely possible that he had a living model to pose for him, had observed the human form with care.

cat. no. 9
fig. 32
fig. 31

☙ *Śrīvijaya* ☙

The rulers of Śrīvijaya, who dominated much of the Malay Peninsula from the 8th to the 13th century, were mainly Mahāyāna Buddhists. They had commercial and cultural relations with Dvāravatī and Cambodia, north and south India, and particularly with Java. The art of the Peninsula, eclectic in character, reveals its indebtedness to these relationships.

figs. 33 to 37

Most of the bronzes are difficult to date with any certainty. One of them, how-

ever, has an inscription on the back in *nāgarī* writing of around the 9th or 10th   *fig. 37*
century. As to the "Buddha of Grahi," discovered at Chaiyâ, the *nāga* bears an inscription dated in 1183. The figure of the Buddha, which is a separate casting, may   *fig. 38*
not be made at the same time; certain things about it suggest a slightly later
date, though the pleated flap of cloth over the left shoulder recalls the Braḥ Meru   *fig. 13*
statue.

1. Various types of Dvāravatī stupa. After stone models and bas-reliefs in the National Museum, Bangkok.

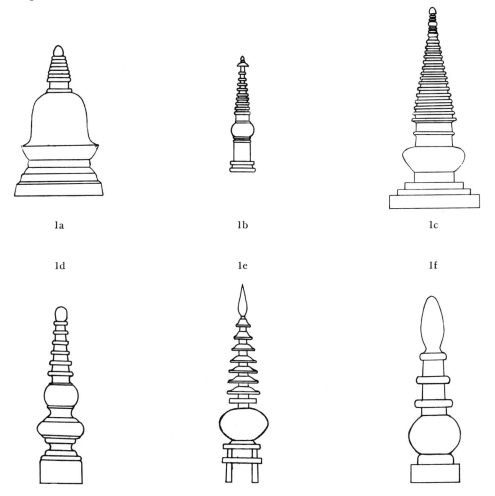

1a   1b   1c

1d   1e   1f

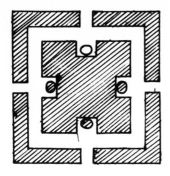

(a) Shrine developed from stupa.

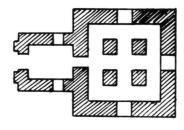

(b) Hollow cube shrine.

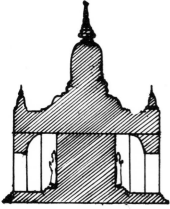

3. Two types of shrine at Pagán, Burma.

4. Stone *maṇḍapa* in the precinct of the Great Relic Monastery, Svargaloka.

5. Architectural fragment representing an aerial palace. Stone; length 110 cm. National Museum, Bangkok. (A part of this fragment is exhibited as Cat. no. 6.)

6. Head of a Buddha image. Stone fragment; ht. 39 cm. (Cat. no. 5.)

7. Detail of a Buddha image. Stone; ht. of complete image, 1.90 m. Monastery of the Excellent Abode (Pavaranivesa), Bangkok. (Note: except for the ear, the restored parts are not shown.)

8   9

8. Standing Buddha. Late Gupta occasional type. Stone relief. Ajanta, India, cave 26. (From Dupont, *Archéologie mône de Dvāravatī*.)

9. Standing Buddha. Stone; ht. 1.90 m. Monastery of the Fifth King (Peñcamapabitra), Bangkok.

10. Standing Buddha. Late Gupta occasional type.
Stone relief. Ajanta, India, cave 19.

11. Standing Buddha. Stone; ht. 1.10 m. Breezewood
Collection, Monkton, Maryland.

12. Standing Buddha. Stone;
ht. 1.08 m. (Cat. no. 2.)

◄ *Opposite:* 13. Buddha seated in the "European" manner. Stone; ht. about 3.70 m. From Wat Braḥ Meru. Now in a chapel of the Braḥ Paṭhama Monastery, Nagara Paṭhama.

14. Buddha seated in the "European" manner. Late Gupta. Stone relief. Ajanta, India, cave 19. *(Photograph by Department of Archaeology, India.)*

15. Votive tablet. Gilt lead; ht. 20 cm. (Cat. no. 135.)

16. Buddha seated on the coiled body of the Nāga king. Stone relief; ht. 75 cm. (Cat. no. 3.)

◄ *Opposite:* 17. The Great Magical Display (below) ; the Buddha preaching in heaven (above) . Gilded stone relief; ht. (excluding frame) 2.40 m. Sudarśana Monastery, Bangkok.

18. Buddha standing on a monster's head. Stone; ht. 47 cm. Private collection, Müang Braḥ Ratha.

19. Buddha image at Wat Kūkuta, Lampûn. Terra cotta; ht. about 1.60 m.

21. Buddha seated in the "European"
manner. Bronze; ht. 14 cm.
(Cat. no. 53.)

22. Standing Buddha. Bronze;
ht. 46.5 cm. (Cat. no. 52.)

23. Standing Buddha. Bronze; ht. 16.3 cm. (Cat. no. 54.)

24. Bust of the Buddha. Bronze fragment; ht. 11.3 cm. (Cat. no. 55.)

25. Head of the Buddha. Terra cotta fragment; ht. 20 cm. National Museum, Bangkok.

63

26. Head of a divinity. Stucco fragment; ht. 12.5 cm.
(Cat. no. 27.)

27. Male figure with animal. Terra cotta; ht. 7 cm.
(Cat. no. 40.)

28. Head of a divinity. Stucco fragment; ht. 15 cm.
(Cat. no. 31.)

29. Head of the Buddha. Terra cotta fragment; ht. 21 cm.
(Cat. no. 36.)

30. Torso of a divinity. Stucco
fragment; ht. 49 cm.
(Cat. no. 28.)

31. Standing divinity. Stone; ht. 98 cm. (Cat. no. 7.)

32. Vishṇu. Stone; ht. 1.50 m. (Cat. no. 8.)

33. The Bodhisattva Avalokiteśvara. Stone; ht. 45 cm. (Cat. no. 10.)

34. Bust of the Buddha. Bronze fragment; ht. 28 cm. (Cat. no. 57.)

36. Tārā. Bronze; ht. 18 cm.
(Cat. no. 60.)

37. Seated Buddha with stand and parasol. 9th-10th
century. Bronze; overall ht. 25 cm. Breezewood
Collection, Monkton, Maryland.

Opposite: 38. Buddha seated on the coiled body of
the Nāga king ("The Buddha of Grahi"). Bronze;
overall ht. 1.62 m. National Museum, Bangkok.

3. The Khmer Period
and the School of Lopburî

THE KHMER dominated central Siam between 1000 and 1250. This was the Angkorian period in Cambodia, the time of their greatest triumphs on the field of battle and in the realm of art. Inheriting and adapting various Indianizing traditions, they built up a brilliant and characteristic culture on very different lines from their neighbors the Mòn of Dvāravatī. In Cambodia the Theravāda was insignificant: the Hindu religions, and later the Mahāyāna, enjoyed royal patronage. The King was a god, an incarnation of Śiva, Vishṇu, or one of the Bodhisattvas. The cult of the God-King was the central fact of Khmer life, the object of vast programs of temple-building, the spiritual power that held the kingdom together. Jealously preserving the heritage of Sanskrit learning, the Brahmins were the priests and astrologers, the philosophers and scientists, the interpreters of the will of the gods.

Sculpture and architecture, in their most serious aspects, were acts of magic. Since *identity* was defined as "name and form" *(nāmarūpa),* a statue could be identified with a donor by giving it some essential relationship to him, such as his exact height, or something of his personal appearance, and at the same time identified with the god of his choice by giving it the proper attributes; then an inscription was added, completing the identification by combining the names of the man and the god: so the donor could be certain of subsequent re-birth as a prince in heaven. Architecture translated into stone the great myths of the Hindu cosmogony and reproduced the world of the gods in the world of men, assuring a perfect correspondence between the two so as to bring prosperity to the kingdom. The temple was an artificial mountain, Meru or Kailāsa, the temporary abode of the god and the permanent repository of the founder's image. Balustrades and doorways, aids in the ascent to heaven, were carved with *nāgas,* symbols of life-giving rain and of the rainbow that is the ladder to heaven. The roofs were mountain peaks, on which *garudas* supported the leafy huts of Brahmin ascetics or bore aloft the aerial palaces of celestials.

Almost nothing is known of the history of Siam during this period. The *Lopburî style* of art, named for the old Mòn city that now became the seat of a Khmer viceroy, continued long after the withdrawal of Khmer power from Siam. It may be dated from the 11th to the 15th century.

❦ Architecture ❧

A FEW MONUMENTS in Siam are of pure Khmer style, hardly to be distinguished from monuments in Cambodia proper. There is no use describing them all; they can best be studied in conjunction with metropolitan Khmer architecture. It will suffice to discuss one of them.

The Mahāyāna Buddhist temple of Pimâi was built in the early 12th century, some years before Angkor Wat. The principal sanctuary is a tower surrounded by *fig. 39* four porches, with a fore-chamber leading into one of them. On the terraces of the pyramidal roof, which is supported by *garudas,* guardian kings are interspersed with *nāgas.* On one of the carved stone door-lintels, a divinity, wearing an elephant *fig. 40* skin upside down, dances on a pair of prostrate figures; on either side is a row of seated Buddhas in royal attire, and a row of dancing celestials below them. On another, the Buddha in royal attire stands in the center of the upper register, flanked *fig. 41* by worshipers, while an orchestra and dancers perform below: the scene perhaps represents the Buddha transformed into the apparition of a Universal Monarch in order to *frighten Jambupati,* a truculent prince who threatened to invade the domains of a peaceful Buddhist king. The stone gallery surrounding the precinct is open on the inner side, with its corbeled roof supported by piers, but closed on the other side by a solid wall; at each of the cardinal points it is interrupted by an elaborate entrance-building of cruciform plan. Enclosing the galleried precinct is a second and larger precinct bounded by a wall.

At various cities in Siam, including Lopburî, are monuments of Khmer style *fig. 42* later modified in the Siamese taste.

Our Exhibition provides some fascinating glimpses of architecture. A bronze *fig. 43* reliquary reproduces in miniature a stupa and its base. A back-frame for an image illustrates the front of a temple with eleven images in niches around a doorway, *fig. 45* and a Bo-tree behind; the missing image would be a copy of the main image in the temple; and though it would in fact stand in front of the frame, anyone familiar with the rules of *explanatory perspective* would understand it to be inside. A bronze shrine with three Buddha images is a copy of a tripartite temple, each section *fig. 46* of which contained a large statue of the Buddha; again, the images must be understood to be inside. A stone relief depicts a pavilion with several persons inside it *fig. 47* (not in front of it, as they appear). In addition to these illustrations, we have two actual fragments of architecture; one of them, a column, is said to come from *cat. no. 16*

cat. no. 15 Pimâi; the other, an antefix, portrays a divinity, presumably Śiva, riding a bull with a single head and two bodies – the form of the animal, I suppose, reproduces in relief some three-dimensional figure which, like an Assyrian bull, was carved to be seen as a complete animal from either side of the corner.

❧ *Sculpture* ☙

THE KHMER SCULPTORS were primarily carvers of stone. When they made bronzes, instead of modeling the clay and wax, they carved it; sharp, crisp detail is the hallmark of their work. The same is often true of the Lopburî school, but not always.

figs. 47, 50 51

figs. 44 and 52

fig. 54

fig. 55

The official art of the period, with its Hindu gods and its creatures of Hindu mythology, reflects the modes of the Khmer capital. So do the splendid ceremonial utensils and fittings for ceremonial vehicles. The Bodhisattvas may be images of royal personages, the males identified as Lokeśvara and the females as Prajñā-pāramitā. Figures of Viśvakarman, the craftsman of the gods and therefore the god of craftsmen, presided over the work of architects and sculptors.

Aside from the official art, the emphasis, and often the manner, of Lopburî sculpture is different from Cambodian. The Dvāravatī tradition was not dead, though the kingdom was extinguished; most of the educated population in Siam were Mòn, and they (unlike the Khmer before the 14th century) must have been for the most part adherents of the Theravāda.

fig. 53

figs. 46, 56, 58

figs. 53, 56

It was therefore natural for the school of Lopburî to produce innumerable images of the Buddha. Standing figures as a rule wear the robe in the covered scheme, seated figures in the open scheme. The prototypes of those that wear the attire of royalty superimposed on the monastic robe were images that had been decked out with real clothes and jewels, originally by devotees of the Mahāyāna; but later, perhaps during the Lopburî period, they became objects of worship in the Theravāda as well. Now and then, like the famous Maṅkuwar Buddha in India, a Buddha image is nude from the waist up, so that it might the more easily be clothed in royal attire of real cloth and gems. The line at the neck, which might be mistaken for the upper hem of a robe in the covered scheme, is really intended to be either the collar-bone or a neck-wrinkle.

figs. 56 and 57

Figures of the Buddha seated on the coiled body of the *nāga* king record an episode in the weeks following the Enlightenment: while the Buddha was in meditative trance, a storm came up; the *nāga*, full of respect for his goodness and observing with alarm his rapt indifference to the rising flood-waters, gently and without disturbing his trance slipped his own serpentine body under him, raising him on his coils above the danger level and spreading his seven-headed hood like an umbrella above. The iconography was well-suited to a land like Cambodia where the ruling family claimed to have sprung from the marriage of a Brahmin to a princess of the *nāgas;* besides, serpent-worshipers who were converted to Buddhism could worship the Sage in this context without running the risk of offending the object of their previous solicitude.

39. Central tower of sanctuary, Pimâi.

42. "The Three Towers" (Brah Prāṅg Sâm Yòt) , Lopburî.

Opposite above: 40. Stone relief; ht. about 90 cm. Lintel over doorway, Pimâi.

Opposite below: 41. Stone relief; ht. about 90 cm. Lintel over doorway, Pimâi.

43. Reliquary. Bronze; ht. 23 cm.
(Cat. no. 109.)

44. Ceremonial utensil. Bronze;
ht. 42 cm. (Cat. no. 110.)

45. Back-frame for an image. Bronze;
ht. 30.5 cm. (Cat. no. 113.)

46. Stand with three Buddha images.
Bronze; ht. 35 cm. (Cat. no. 63.)

47. Figures seated in a pavilion. Red sandstone relief; ht. 60 cm.; w. 69 cm. (Cat. no. 14.)

48. Pedestal. Bronze; ht. 12 cm. (Cat. no. 115.)

49. Pedestal. Bronze; ht. 25.5 cm. (Cat. no. 114.)

50. Dancing figure. Bronze; ht. 10.3 cm.
(Cat. no. 71.)

51. Garuda with Nāga. Bronze; ht. 45 cm.
(Cat. no. 73.)

53. Standing Buddha. Bronze; ht. 64.7 cm.
(Cat. no. 61.)

54. Prajñāpāramitā. Bronze; ht. 18.2 cm.
(Cat. no. 66.)

55. Viśvakarman. Bronze; ht. 11.3 cm. (Cat. no. 69.)

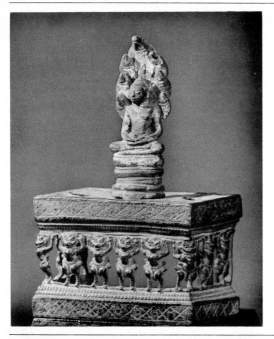

57. Seated Buddha on pedestal. Bronze; ht. 20 cm. (Cat. no. 62.)

58. Seated Buddha. Stone; ht. 88 cm. (Cat. no. 12.)

59. Jar. Terra cotta; ht. 53 cm. (Cat. no. 178.)

60. Spouted pot. Terra cotta; ht. 12 cm.
(Cat. no. 182.)

61. Covered jar. Terra cotta; ht. 15 cm.
(Cat. no. 183.)

4. Sukhodaya

THE TAI had long been settled in southern and southwestern China, where they were a numerous minority. Some of them, seeking richer lands and freedom from Chinese domination, drifted into Southeast Asia. We first hear of them, under the name *Syām,* in an 11th century inscription discovered in Vietnam; in the next century *Syām* contingents appear in the procession of Khmer troops and their vassals in a bas-relief at Angkor Wat.

The region of Sukhodaya and Svargaloka, where these Tai-Syām had been recruited, was a distant outpost of the Khmer Empire. Here, some time in the first half of the 13th century, two Tai lords renounced their allegiance to the Khmer and made the province an independent kingdom. King Râm Kamhèng, the son of one of these lords, expanded the kingdom until it included most of Siam except the northern provinces.

At Sukhodaya Siamese culture developed rapidly. The Tai had learned all sorts of material techniques from the Khmer. They had adopted the religion of the Mòn. Through the Mòn country, and through Nagara Śrī Dharmarāja, they made contact with Ceylon, the fountainhead of the Theravāda, and invited numerous Sinhalese monks to come and settle in Sukhodaya. Our chief sources of information on these matters are the stone inscriptions left by Râm Kamhèng (1292) and his successors.

Râm Kamhèng's conquests permanently established the supremacy of the Tai in Siam, but his own kingdom lost most of the conquered territories after his death. In the second half of the 14th century it was a vassal of Ayudhyā, and in the 15th it was incorporated into that kingdom.

The profound originality of Sukhodaya art lies not in the invention of meaningless new forms, but in harmonious eclecticism. Except in ceramics, it is hard to see any Chinese influence. The architecture contains reminiscences of several Indianizing traditions, while the statuary carries to a logical conclusion the fluent style of Gupta India.

Architecture

WHILE THE MONUMENTS of the Tai kingdom cannot for a moment compete with Angkor in grandeur, they have a particular kind of beauty that Angkor lacks. In contrast to massive stone, brick and stucco are well suited to the Theravāda with its doctrine of impermanence.

The stupas are of numerous types. One has an octagonal terrace at the bottom which suggests a Mòn origin. Of the bell-shaped stupas, one type is of modest size and plain design; another, standing on a truncated pyramid, has a fluted dome that *fig. 62* looks like a cloth-covered reliquary; a third, standing on a base supported by *fig. 63* masonry elephants, is clearly inspired by the Mahāthūpa at Anurādhapura, the *fig. 64* holiest monument in Ceylon. The stupa-form most characteristic of Sukhodaya is vaguely reminiscent of a minaret; very likely it is copied from a little bronze *fig. 65* votive stupa, such as those discovered at Negapatam in southern India.

The type of structure called *prāṅg* is a Tai imitation of a Khmer tower, though *fig. 66* not a very exact one. Re-entrants have eaten the corners away until the cross-section is almost round; stone is replaced by brick or laterite and stucco; the terraces are more numerous and less distinctive; and the sculptured animals and pavilions on them have atrophied into geometric antefixes.

Why such heterogeneous forms? Clearly it is because the founders liked to copy monuments that had a reputation for holiness and beauty – or, to put it differently, for age and authenticity. If the originals were far away, small models could be sent for and then copied on a larger scale. That seems to be what happened at the "Seven Rows of Reminders" at Svargaloka, where monuments of a dozen or more different forms are lined up one after another. In the present state of our studies we cannot identify their prototypes, so we cannot tell how accurate the copies were. But we can be sure they were more accurate than the purported views of famous monuments in Ceylon that a 19th-century painter in Bangkok provides in a picture *cat. no. 246* in our Exhibition. It is easy to smile at a painter who had no idea of the originals and made them all exactly alike, contenting himself by writing the different names under them. Yet the parallel is instructive: neither the builder nor the painter intended to provide material for a text-book on architecture; both were making Reminders.

If the importation of small models can determine *type*, though with doubtful precision, the importation of craftsmen can have a very marked effect on *style*. We know from an inscription that craftsmen from Ceylon helped to rebuild the Great Relic Monastery at Sukhodaya in the 14th century; and some of the arches there, *fig. 69* with their inward-turning water-monsters (*makara*), are pure Sinhalese.

Apart from the solid monuments, the precincts of a monastery included various other sorts of structure. The monks presumably lived in huts of wood or basketry, of which no trace remains. The *maṇḍapa*, built to house a Footprint or a cult-

fig. 4

image, was a hollow cube with a pyramidal roof; an example at Svargaloka, restored in modern times, gives a good idea of its appearance; the larger examples, such as Wat Sî Chum at Sukhodaya, have unfortunately lost their roofs. The inspiration for this sort of building, I think, was Mòn, just as it was for similar buildings at Pagán. The assembly-hall *(vihāra)*, as well as its almost identical twin the ordination-hall *(uposatha)*, was a long nave with stuccoed brick walls and a tile

fig. 67

roof: a simple form can be seen, probably with little alteration, at Nagara Svarga. In a more elaborate form, the nave was flanked by a pair of side-aisles, or even two or three pairs, separated by the rows of columns that supported the roof.

Monastery precincts, or parts of them, could be enclosed in various ways – bamboo fences, brick walls, or cloister-like galleries. The Great Relic at Svargaloka is surrounded by a laterite railing, probably built in the late 13th century, consisting of a coping supported by columns more than a yard in diameter. The theme may have been inspired, at least indirectly, by Ceylon; but the gates, topped by Khmer towers with faces in the superstructure, were surely inspired by the Bayon at Angkor.

cat. nos. 46 and 136

Several objects in the Exhibition help us to visualize the architecture. Two of them are illustrations of shrines, with the architectural trim clearly shown; the vases of flowers should be understood not as part of the structure but as real objects offered by the pious. Carved stone was seldom used, but we are fortunate in having

cat. no. 17

one elegant example in the Exhibition. While stucco was the usual material for

fig. 70

exterior detail, ceramics often replaced it: the head of a *nāga* is one of a pair that stood at the lower corners of a pediment while their bodies writhed upward toward the apex.

Palaces were made of wood. None have survived, but there are two or three

fig. 68

drawings in the Jātaka series from Wat Sî Chum that illustrate them.

⑥ *Images of the Buddha* ⑨

THE SUKHODAYA SCULPTORS were modelers rather than carvers, preferring bronze for *ronde-bosse,* and stucco for reliefs. The first masters from whom they learned the art of image-making were doubtless Mòn practitioners of the late Dvāravatī style, and to some extent Khmer practitioners of the post-Bayon school. Sinhalese artists, arriving after the Sukhodaya plastic style was established, helped to refine and perfect it. We might guess that technicians from south India also taught at Sukhodaya: the three-dimensional quality and the fluency of Tai bronzes suggests their example.

Some writers maintain that there was an earlier school of Tai sculpture at

Chieng Sèn which played a part in the formation of the Sukhodaya style; but I believe the works they attribute to that school are of much later date (see page 123).
The debt to Nagara Śrī Dharmarāja, which is sometimes proposed, is difficult to
assess, as we do not know what its art was at that time: if it still held reminiscences
of the earlier Buddhist art of Java, it may have contributed to the tranquil plas-
ticity of Sukhodaya sculpture. But that is ultimately the legacy of the Indian late
Gupta, and it may equally well have been transmitted to the Tai by other inter-
mediaries. In any case the sources to which Sukhodaya is most immediately in-
debted are the Mòn, the Khmer, and the Sinhalese.

We do not know when the school of Sukhodaya sculpture started, but we know
from Râm Kamhèng's inscription that it was producing in quantity before the
close of the 13th century. It continued well into the 16th, and perhaps longer. Its
output, which ranges in quality from folk-art to the most accomplished masterpieces, includes thousands of images of life-size or larger, and incalculable numbers
of statuettes.

Out of this enormous mass of sculpture, hardly a half-dozen images can be
dated with certainty. To establish some sort of chronological framework, we can
postulate a *pre-classic* style, assignable to the 13th century, a *high classic* dating
mainly in the 14th, and a *post-classic* in the 15th and 16th. This is a purely arbitrary division, the usefulness of which remains to be tested.

Walking figures. The most astonishing invention of Sukhodaya sculpture, and
the glory of Siamese art, is the walking Buddha *en ronde bosse*. Because of the
difficulty of the subject, first-rate examples are rare. The great majority seem to be
rather off balance. This is true of the example in our Exhibition; and its attenuated   *cat. no. 77*
proportions suggest the post-classic.

The walking Buddha – or, to be more precise, the Buddha who has just come
to a pause in walking – is most beautifully represented by a statue, of somewhat
more than life-size, in the Monastery of the Fifth King. The surface of the bronze is   *fig. 72*
a deep brown color, with traces of gilding. Except for the head-flame, which is a
restoration and not quite the right shape, this statue typifies all the most remarkable qualities of the high classic.

The anatomy, with its unexpected proportions and auspicious marks, typifies
the physical and mental development of the Yogi. Several of its features correspond
to those curious descriptions of the Buddha's person given in the Pali commentaries
composed in medieval Ceylon. The shoulders are broad, the chest full, and the
arms very long; the footsoles are flat and the heels projecting. Other features are
based on the stereotyped similes used in Sanskrit poetry to describe gods and
heroes, or (what amounts to the same thing) comparisons with familiar objects pre-

scribed in the Indian art manuals as guides to anatomical form. The legs are *like the legs of a deer,* and the thighs *like the stems of banana-trees.* The arms are *smooth and rounded, like the trunk of an elephant;* the hands are *like lotus flowers just beginning to open,* with the finger-tips turning backward like petals. The shape of the head is *like an egg;* the chin, with its incised oval line, is *like a mango stone;* the nose is *like a parrot's beak* and the eyebrows *like drawn bows.* The curls of the hair are *like the stings of scorpions.* At the same time, without making any attempt at realism, the artist has put something of the Tai physiognomy into the inflection of eyelids and lips, the slim hands and the tapering fingers; and the vigorous abdominal muscles recall the prolonged breathing exercises that precede meditation.

The modeling has a trance-like quality. The material is knowingly used, but not to give the illusion of flesh and drapery. This is not the likeness of a man clad in stuff, it is the likeness of a vision of fiery energy. The surfaces of the bronze flicker, the silhouette leaps like a fire.

Whereas most Buddha images, being designed to be seen mainly from the front, are not particularly interesting when looked at from the side or the back, this statue looks superb from any angle, and best of all when seen, as circumambulants would see it, from every angle in succession.

We shall seek in vain for the prototype of the bronze walking Buddhas if we insist that it should be a walking figure *en ronde bosse:* there was no such thing until Sukhodaya invented it. The prototype can only have been a relief, and the most natural place for us to look for it would be in the Sukhodaya pre-classic. The

fig. 73   figure that best meets the conditions is a colossal stucco high-relief, over 20 feet tall, which on the basis of certain historical evidences we can probably date in the late 13th century. Its size and its beauty would make it a likely model for copying; and if we compare it point by point with the bronze statue, we shall see how similar the iconography is. A copy is no less valid for being in a different medium: from the point of view of orthodoxy, stucco and bronze are interchangeable. For cult images, the Tai preferred bronze, and bronze invites *ronde bosse.* That, I suppose, is how the walking Buddha came to emerge from relief into the full round. By tracing our statue's ancestry back one generation, we have explained in some measure what is in *our* eyes a startlingly original invention.

The next thing we have to explain is the origin of the colossal stucco walking Buddha, which is itself a novelty. Why was it invented? And what is it a copy of?

We can answer the first question easily. Buddhist literature lists four postures (*iryāpatha*) in which the Buddha may be depicted – walking, standing, seated and reclining. We know the list aroused the interest of the Sukhodaya sculptors, or of their patrons, because at certain monuments each of the four postures is illustrated by a large stucco figure on one of the four walls. This was the first time that sculpture needed to make a sharp distinction between the walking Buddha and the Buddha standing still. Previously the only figures of the walking Buddha were in scenes from his life, in which the action would indicate the distinction well enough; but as soon as they were removed from their context the posture had to be shown in a way that would leave no possible doubt. That is manifestly the reason for images like the colossal stucco.

In order to find the model they are based on, we shall have to look for a figure wearing the robe in the same way and having the hands in a similar position. We therefore have to reject the only surviving examples of the walking Buddha in Dvāravatī art, which are the miraculous apparitions in the stone reliefs of the *great magical display* (e.g. the outward-turning figure in fig. 17). On the same ground we have to reject the few Khmer reliefs of the walking Buddha, and the innumerable Javanese reliefs of the same subject. The figures that best fill the conditions are in the stone reliefs of the *descent from heaven* in the Ananda temple at Pagán (here the context rather than the leg-position denotes walking, or a momentary pause in walking). I do not think it likely that these figures furnished the model, but their existence shows that the theme was well-known to Mòn sculptors; so we can be confident that there were examples, now vanished, in Dvāravatī art.

Robe in the open scheme, left hand up, right hand down: we have seen this combination before. It is the late Gupta *standard* type of the cave-temples (page 43). In order to simplify matters, let us compare it directly with the Sukhodaya bronze walking Buddha. The resemblance is striking, both in iconography and in spirit. In both cases the left leg supports the weight of the body; and if the *hanchement* is less noticeable in the bronze image when seen from the front, there is something very like it when seen from an angle. Some of the figures in the cave-temples are standing still, some are walking; the distinction is not very obvious, for both feet rest securely on the ground, though sometimes they point in a way that shows the act of walking is to be understood. In the cave-temples that was sufficient; but at Sukhodaya, to sharpen the distinction, the right heel is raised. In both cases the right arm hangs down and the left is lifted, but their function is different: in the Indian image the right hand performs the gesture and the left grasps the robe, whereas in the Sukhodaya statue the right arm swings free and the left hand is made to perform the gesture; a similar change in the function of the hands, without much change in their position, had occurred in Dvāravatī art in a different context (page 44). In both cases the robe is in the open scheme; but the Sukhodaya bronze has a shoulder-flap, while the Indian image has none. It is the

fig. 74

fig. 13

fig. 74
fig. 72

figs. 9,
11, 12

fig. 81

fig. 76

same thing as the pleated shoulder-flap of the colossal stucco and the Braḥ Meru Buddha, but further stylized. Where the cloth falls from the raised forearm in the Indian image, an undulating line denotes the hem of the pleats pulled out of place by the upward tension; in the Sukhodaya bronze the pleats are omitted, and only an undulating silhouette remains: what could be more appropriate than such a fluttering of cloth for a walking figure that has just come to a halt? A similar re-interpretation had already occurred in Dvāravatī art. As to the lower termination of the pleats, Dvāravatī used often to render them as a neat little pattern at the lower corner of the robe, and Sukhodaya reduces the pattern to a tiny hook. This hook is worth remembering, for it is a hallmark of Sukhodaya workmanship.

In short, the differences between the Indian image and its remote descendant at Sukhodaya can be explained on the basis of a vanished intermediary in Dvāra-vatī art – a stone relief analogous to those at Pagán, representing the *descent from heaven,* or its counterpart in stucco.

In most of the Sukhodaya walking Buddhas, as in this one, the left hand per-forms the gesture and the left leg supports the weight of the body. Less frequently the right hand performs the gesture and the right leg supports the body. The dif-ference, seemingly trivial, betrays an origin in a totally different model. It would take too long to trace its ultimate source, which is perhaps Mathurā; but the inter-mediary was a type well known in Dvāravatī bronzes.

Standing figures. Images of the Buddha standing still are rare in the high clas-sic, at least in bronze; but there are some fine examples in stucco. In the post-classic, on the other hand, there are a great many examples in bronze. One of the finest, a Buddha wearing a crown but not the rest of the royal attire, is in our Ex-hibition. Though crowned Buddhas are rare in Sukhodaya art, it is clearly a work of that school. We can be sure from the face, the suave modeling, and especially the "hallmark" in the form of the little hooks at the lower corners of the robe. I should guess this figure ought to be dated in the 15th century, a time when Sukhodaya had already lost its political independence but not its artistic inspiration.

We might expect that the Buddha would be dressed in the same way when standing still as when walking; or if not, that he would wear the robe in the open scheme when standing, as monks wear it inside the monastery, and in the covered scheme when walking, as monks wear it when going out; but we have just the op-posite. The undergarment, too, is differently arranged: the hem at the waist is turned down over an invisible belt, and a panel of folded cloth falls down between the legs; the result is a large T-shaped or Y-shaped pattern that looks as if it were part of the robe, but of course it is really part of the undergarment seen through the robe's transparency. The arrangement is perfectly feasible, and is in fact the rule in many Siamese monasteries today. It appears now and then in Dvāravatī bronzes and stuccos, and often in Khmer art.

While they are chiefly to be explained by the power of the prototype, these apparently illogical differences in dress offered a special advantage to the first school of sculpture that made a sharp distinction between the walking Buddha and the Buddha standing still: there could be no mistake about the posture even if the feet were hidden.

The same is true of the hand positions, but to a less extent. The standing figures, like the walking, can perform a gesture with either hand; but, unlike them, they can also perform it with both, or not at all.

fig. 75

Seated figures. The great majority of Sukhodaya images are in the seated posture. They wear the monastic dress in exactly the same way as the walking Buddha. As in Sinhalese and Khmer sculpture, the legs are folded, one lying on top of the other in the *hero position.* With very few exceptions, the right hand is in the position of *calling the Earth to witness:* the theme is too common in earlier sculpture for us to be able to point to a specific prototype, but not common enough to explain its overwhelming predominance in Sukhodaya art. At their best the seated figures of the high classic style have the same plastic qualities as the walking ones. Although the interest of momentarily arrested motion is absent, the nervous energy is still there. In their own way, they are just as flame-like.

figs. 77 and 78

The famous image called the *Victorious King* is post-classic. It is supposed to have been cast around 1350, but the only thing we can be sure of is that it was already in existence before 1438. In accordance with the commentarial description of the Buddha's person – or rather in accordance with a particular interpretation that was ignored by the high classic – the four fingers of each hand are of equal length. Sweetness of expression here replaces spiritual vitality; the contours of the body are more static than flickering. The tongue of flame attached to the top of the head springs from no inner fire.

While most of the post-classic seated Buddhas have about the same iconography, with or without the equal fingers, Sukhodaya also produced a few examples of the *lion type* (see page 123). I think it probable that the type was introduced at Sukhodaya at about the same time as at Chieng Mai, that is, around the year 2000 of the Buddhist Era (1456/7 A. D.). As to the example in our Exhibition, I should date it in the second half of the 15th century. True, the style of writing on its pedestal has been adduced as an argument in favor of dating it in the late 13th or early 14th century; but the Sukhodaya script of the late 13th century has the vowels written

fig. 79

quite differently, and the script used here, while first attested around the mid-14th century, was still being used as late as the 16th. The argument, therefore, does not seem very compelling.

cat. no. 76
fig. 80

Reclining figures. This is the least numerous class. The example in our Exhibition is of indifferent quality, and should perhaps be assigned to the post-classic.

The best example of the high classic is in the Excellent Abode Monastery. It shows the virtuosity of the artist in converting seeming absurdities into peculiar beauties. In accordance with a custom that began at Gandhāra, such an image must be conceived as an image of the standing Buddha laid down upon its right side. In this case, curiously enough, the theoretical model is not a Sukhodaya standing Buddha, but a model wearing the robe in the open scheme such as inspired the walking Buddhas. The projecting skirts of the robe at the upper side rise into the air, in defiance of gravity, because they floated out to the left of the leg when the figure was upright. With consummate skill the artist has prevented them from looking foolish: he has made them look miraculous.

Dated images. Only five Sukhodaya images are known that can be positively dated by means of inscriptions on their pedestals.

fig. 81

Four of them, three walking and one standing, belong to a group cast in the town of Nân in 1426. Two of the walking figures (one illustrated) were perhaps made by the same artist; they seem very close to the high classic, though certain details relate them to the *Victorious King*. The third walking figure (not illustrated) and the standing one appear to be the work of a different hand; if we did not know they were made at the same time as the first two, we would probably ascribe them to a later date.

fig. 75

fig. 82

A seated image of unknown provenance, now in a monastery in Tonburî, is dated four years earlier, in 1422. It is certainly post-classic, though it is really not such a poor piece of work as it now appears: misguided piety has scraped off the patina and given the surface a very unpleasant high polish.

⚅ Hindu Gods ⚆

A BUDDHIST MONARCH is the defender of all religions, not merely his own. The Kings of Sukhodaya had subjects of Hindu faith; in particular, they had Brahmin advisors, who needed temples and images. A mid-14th century inscription refers to the installation of images of Śiva and Vishṇu in the Brahmin temple. That is perhaps the date that should be assigned to the two magnificent bronzes in our Exhibition.

fig. 83

⚔ *Stucco* ⚕

IF THE STUCCOES of Dvāravatī and Ceylon are lively and expressive, those of Sukhodaya are positively exuberant, ranging from the grotesque and the humorous to the graceful and the sublime.

The only example in our Exhibition is a head from a Buddha image. Such *cat. no. 45* fragments are hard to assign a date to; but I see no reason to believe it any earlier than the colossal stucco figure we have already examined (page 92), and it may be much later.

A 14th-century stucco relief, still *in situ* at Sukhodaya, represents the *nativity*. *fig. 84* The Buddha's mother, leaning on her sister for support, grasps the tree-branch with one hand; Ceylon has inspired the tense posture of her legs, and it may also have inspired the costumes.

Another scene at the same monument, presumably of the same date but later repaired, represents the *death of the Buddha*. Two of his disciples give way to extrav- *fig. 85* agant despair, but another, who has attained complete detachment, sits in quiet meditation. The arch above the scene is entirely Sinhalese. (Cf. page 89).

One of the most beautiful works of Buddhist art in the world, in spite of the damage it has suffered, is a plaster relief of the *descent from heaven* on the wall of *fig. 86* a ruined monument near Sukhodaya. The central figure is the exact counterpart of the colossal stucco and the high classic bronze we have studied, which leads us to believe that they too, and indeed all the Sukhodaya figures having the robe in the open scheme with the left hand up and the right hand down, signify the descent from heaven. The plaster was originally gilded and painted in various colors; but now most of the paint has worn off, except the red on the Buddha's robe, which has faded to a soft pink. The relief shows the easy and graceful movement of the Sage, decked out in the splendor of his supernatural anatomy, descending the miraculously created stairway, while Indra and Brahmā hold parasols over his head. The gods and their followers are dressed in princely costumes, which are probably very much like the costumes worn at the Sukhodaya Court on ceremonial occasions, though perhaps they are partly copied from Ceylon. In a sort of gallery above, the gods who remain in heaven look down upon the scene. All the gods wear an expression of pious satisfaction – not in the least mystical or austere, but happy and respectful. The artist has made the scene majestic, but at the same time delightfully cheerful and good-natured.

We have already seen the virtuosity of the stucco-workers in architectural detail. Now and then a demon's head strongly recalls Dvāravatī. One monument is sup- *fig. 87* ported by straining dwarfs, richly-dressed little earth-spirits in attitudes of pure

fig. 88

fig. 89

comedy. Another is upheld by *garudas*, symbols of the aerial world, standing on elephants, symbols of earth; while divinities hold aloft vases of flowers, symbols of plenty, in one pair of hands, pressing the palms of the other pair together in front of them in an attitude of worship. A frieze of walking monks surrounds the base of the main sanctuary of the Great Relic at Sukhodaya. Elsewhere, a worshiping monk is affectionately remembered in an adroit sketch.

❆ *Footprints* ❆

ACCORDING TO LEGEND the Buddha flew to Ceylon by the power of his fiery energy and stamped the impression of his footsole in the rock on top of Adam's Peak, to remain forever "as a seal to show that Ceylon is the inheritance of the Buddha and that his religion will here flourish."

One of the kings of Sukhodaya, an inscription tells us, sent an emissary to Ceylon to take an impression of the Footprint, and then had copies made "in conformity with the original." Another caused a slab of stone to be engraved with "pictures of the Lord's two feet, similar and conforming in measure to the holy Footprint on Adam's Peak;" and the inscription adds that these pictures were "resplendent with the eminent mark of the Wheel, and covered with the 108 auspicious signs."

The Sukhodaya Footprints indeed "conform in measure" to the original – the length, about two yards, is proportionate to the 30-foot stature that legend ascribes to the Sage – but in appearance they are no more like it than they are like a human

cf. fig. 90
and cat.
no. 246

foot. On the contrary, they are huge diagrams, incised or raised in relief, on stone or metal tablets. The wheel occupies the middle; within it in concentric circles, or else outside it in a checkerboard pattern, are the 108 symbols. Since the grouping varies so much in different examples, it is plain that they are by no means accurate copies of any one model, let alone the print on Adam's Peak – they are inspired simply by the list given in the Pali texts.

The 108 signs recall the paraphernalia of divination by podoscopy. As palmistry relies on an inspection of the lines and creases in the hand, so podoscopy relies on an inspection of the lines and creases in the footsole. And as a palmist's chart might use little pictures instead of letters to label the *mountain of Mercury* or the *mountain of the moon,* so the diagrammatic Footprints perhaps derive ultimately from ancient podoscopic charts in which the 108 signs were labels of auspicious skin formations.

But they have another significance as well. They are a condensed gazetteer of the universe – sixteen upper heavens with their Brahmā gods; six lower heavens with their Devas; the stars and the planets; the earth with its geography and samples of the good things it contains. Here is Mount Meru, surrounded by seven concentric rock-walled seas, here are the four great continents with their associated islands, here are the seven great rivers and lakes. Here are the flora and fauna of good omen, the regalia of benevolent kings, and the ritual utensils of holy monks. Since the Buddha wears all these things on his footsole, they are subordinate to him and support him; they are but small items in the encyclopedia of his boundless wisdom; they announce his utterly exceptional character.

When the Buddha wishes to signify that a land *is his inheritance* he places this prodigious seal upon it. And when a ruler wishes to signify that in his land *the Buddha's religion will flourish,* he can hardly do better than to install such seals on hilltops near his principal cities.

62. Stupa on the Lesser Footprint Hill, Sukhodaya.

63. The Elephant-
Supported Stupa,
Sukhodaya.

64. Model of the
Mahāthūpa, Anurādhapura,
Ceylon.

65. Central shrine of the Great Relic Monastery, Sukhodaya.

66. *Prāṅg* of the Great Relic Monastery, Svargaloka.

70. Architectural fragment. Glazed ceramic; ht. 61 cm. (Cat. no. 186.)

71. Demon head. Glazed ceramic; ht. 17.5 cm. (Cat. no. 187.)

73. Walking Buddha. Stucco relief; ht. about 7 metres. Great Relic Monastery, Svargaloka.

◄*Opposite:* 72. Walking Buddha. Bronze; ht. about 2.20 m. Monastery of the Fifth King (Peñcamapabitra) , Bangkok. (Note: the flame on top of the head is a modern restoration; the original must have been more like that in Fig. 77.)

74. Standing (or walking) Buddha. Late Gupta standard type. Kanheri, India.

75. Standing Buddha. Cast in 1426. Bronze;
ht. 1.90 m. Elephant Monastery, Nân.

76. Standing Buddha. Bronze;
ht. 1.87 m. (Cat. no. 94.)

77. Seated Buddha. Bronze; ht. 94 cm.
Collection of H.R.H. Prince Chalermbol
Yugala, Bangkok.

78. Seated Buddha. Bronze; ht. 60 cm.
(Cat. no. 75.)

80. Reclining Buddha. Bronze; length 3.50 m. Excellent Abode Monastery (Pavaranivesa), Bangkok.

Opposite: 81.   Walking Buddha. Cast in 1426. Bronze; ht. 1.86 m. P' yâ Pû Monastery, Nân.

82. Seated Buddha. Cast in 1422. Bronze; ht. about 1.50 m. Haṁsa Monastery (Wat Hong),
Tonburî.

84. The Nativity. Stucco relief. Great Relic Monastery, Sukhodaya.

85. Death of the Buddha. Stucco relief. Great Relic Monastery, Sukhodaya.

86. The Descent from Heaven. Stucco relief; ht. about 4 m. Monastery of the Coral-Tree Pond, Sukhodaya.

117

87. Fragment of sculpture from a monument. Stucco. Field office of the Archeological Service, Sukhodaya.

88. Frieze of walking monks. Stucco. Great Relic Monastery, Sukhodaya.

89. Fragment of sculpture from a monument. Stucco. Field office of the Archeological Service, Sukhodaya.

90. The 108 Signs. Mid-19th century. Mother-of pearl and black lacquer on Footsoles of colossal
reclining Buddha. Length of foot about 6 metres. Bo-Tree Monastery, Bangkok.

91. Three maternity figurines.
Glazed ceramic; average ht. 10.5 cm.
(Cat. no. 184.)

92. Figure of a hunchback. Glazed ceramic; ht. 15.3 cm.
(Cat. no. 185.)

93. Water-bottle. Glazed ceramic; ht. 21.5 cm.
(Cat. no. 198.)

5. Northern Siam

FROM THE LATE 13th century to the mid-16th, northern Siam was the seat of the independent kingdom of Lân Nâ.

The earlier history is obscure. According to the *Chieng Sèn theory,* which was evolved several dozen years ago, the Tai had ruled a part of the region, including Chieng Sèn, as early as the 9th century; in the 11th they submitted to King Aniruddha of Pagán, who introduced Theravāda Buddhism; and in the 12th, or perhaps long before, Chieng Sèn was a flourishing center of Buddhist art.

In fact there is no evidence whatever that Aniruddha or any of his dynasty conquered any part of northern Siam, or introduced the Theravāda there. The old Mòn kingdom of Lampûn, a stronghold of the Doctrine, was almost certainly the only place in the north where the arts were cultivated on any considerable scale before the 14th century. In 1292 the Tai, who had been ruling at Chieng Sèn for several generations, conquered the old Mòn city and possessed themselves of its skilled artisans. Four years later they founded a new capital at Chieng Mai.

The Tai rulers of Lân Nâ, with one exception, were staunch Buddhists. In the 14th century the religious and artistic influence of Sukhodaya made itself felt. In the early 15th, there was a setback, when the reigning monarch renounced the Doctrine and expropriated the monasteries, transferring his worship to the spirits and his support to the sorcerers. He was deposed in 1441 and his son Tiloka mounted the throne. Tiloka was not only a devout Buddhist; he was also a man of great energy, strong will, and varied interests. Under his sponsorship the golden age of Buddhist art and letters at Chieng Mai began. It lasted about a hundred years. In the mid-16th century the Burmese conquered Lân Nâ and held the greater part of it for three hundred years. In the 19th it became a part of Siam.

ⓖ *Architecture* ⓐ

THE OLDEST TAI MONUMENT in Lân Nâ that remains standing is the Cetiya Sî *fig. 94* Liem ("the Four-Square Reminder") near Chieng Mai, built around 1300. Though it has undergone some deplorable modernization, it retains enough of its original shape to show that it was a copy of some Mòn monument at Lampûn, such as Wat Kūkuṭa.

fig. 95   The seven Spires Monastery (Wat Jet Yòt), begun in 1455, is the masterpiece of Tiloka's reign. The founder, it may be guessed, intended it as a great act of merit in connection with the 2000th anniversary of the Buddha's death (1456/7). Officially named *Mahābodhārāma*, it is a copy of the Mahābodhi temple at Bodhgayā on a smaller scale; very likely Tiloka, like his fellow-monarch the Mòn King of Pegu, sent a mission of architects and craftsmen to India to get the plans. As at Bodhgayā, the main structure is a cube, supporting a large central obelisk with a lesser obelisk *fig. 97* at each corner. The stucco patterns on the obelisks, manifestly intended to reproduce the false-dormers and other details of the original, were perhaps in fact copied *fig. 96* from a small replica of the sort which has been discovered in considerable quantity in the temple precinct at Bodhgayā. On the walls are stucco reliefs of the greatest *fig. 98* elegance, clearly inspired by Sukhodaya; celestial beings float among flowers, press- *fig. 99* ing their palms together in the gesture of respect. Nominally they are the gods that came to applaud the Buddha's victory over evil; in fact, as they are dressed in the ceremonial costume of the Court of Lân Nâ, they are doubtless idealized portraits of King Tiloka and the members of his family. There was nothing like this at Bodhgayā; but their presence here does not in the least violate the rule of copying: they are not thought of as an integral part of the monument, but as real people in the guise of gods.

The old monuments of Lân Nâ have suffered terribly from the ravages of war, and even worse from the piety that likes to have objects of worship look as spick and span as possible. As it is difficult to draw the right conclusions from structures that have been so much restored, the bronze models are more instructive, especially when they are inscribed with a date: one of the most beautiful was cast by a Burmese official at Chieng Sèn in the year 1727. The example in our Exhibition is no *cat. no. 125* less charming; and as it is similar in certain details it may date from about the same time.

Assembly-halls and other monastery buildings of light construction are perishable; probably the oldest that now survive date from the late 18th century, but the 19th and even the 20th have produced some fine work, notable for the elegance of its woodcarving.

❝ Sculpture ❞

THE ENTIRE RANGE of art in northern Siam (with the partial exception of Lampûn) is commonly attributed to "the Chieng Sèn style," though no one claims that more than a fraction of it has anything to do with Chieng Sèn.

This fraction consists of several hundred bronze Buddha images of a single *fig. 100* type. (The same type was also produced, though more rarely, at Sukhodaya; see page 95). The posture is seated, with the legs crossed and both feet turned up in the *adamantine pose,* and with the right hand *calling the Earth to witness.* The robe is in the open scheme and the shoulder-flap ends above the nipple. The finial on top of the head is a lotus-bud.

In honor of the most famous example, an image at Chieng Mai called the *Lion Lord* (Pra Sing), I shall refer to the group of images having these particular characteristics as the *lion type.* Up to a few years ago all the images of this type were assigned to the *early Chieng Sèn style* and dated anywhere from the 9th to the 13th century; but when it was noticed that a certain number of them bear dated inscriptions, and that the dates range from 1470 to 1565, the advocates of the Chieng Sèn theory decided that they were of *early Chieng Sèn type* but *later Chieng Sèn style;* while those without inscriptions, or at least the most beautiful among them, were of *early Chieng Sèn type* and *early Chieng Sèn style* as well.

Another type, of which there are many thousands of examples, is also seated and *calling the Earth to witness;* but the legs, instead of being crossed, are folded in the *hero pose.* The robe again is in the open scheme, but the shoulder-flap comes all *fig. 101* the way down to the navel. The finial on top of the head is a flame. As the iconography comes from Sukhodaya, everyone agrees that this type dates from the 14th century or later, and that the center of production was Chieng Mai; to distinguish it from the other, it is commonly assigned to the *later Chieng Sèn style,* or, more correctly, to the *Chieng Mai style.* The same style includes images of other types, with several variations in dress, posture, and hand position; and though seated figures are the most frequent, there are also standing, walking and reclining ones. I shall call them all *mixed types.*

I have adopted such non-committal names in order to spare the reader the discomfort of a contradictory terminology. In my opinion the lion type ("early Chieng Sèn") and the mixed types ("later Chieng Sèn") are more or less contemporary, both beginning in the second half of the 15th century. As they both centered at Chieng Mai there is no good reason to associate either of them particularly with Chieng Sèn. Chieng Sèn was the second city of Lân Nâ in the golden age, and all types were made there – as indeed they were at Lampûn and several other cities in the same period – but the capital, Chieng Mai, was naturally the leader.

There is no use repeating here the reasons why I think the Chieng Sèn theory is wrong, nor explaining the reasons why many of my friends in Bangkok think it is right; it will suffice to refer the curious reader to other works for the arguments on both sides.* In the following pages I shall merely summarize my views of the probabilities regarding the development of sculpture in the north.

We have already noticed the Mòn style of Lampûn (8th-13th century), an off-shoot of Dvāravatī art. If the Tai of Chieng Sèn were making any images at that time, it seems likely they would be of a similar sort. Several small bronzes have been found in various parts of the north that might answer that description, though none, I believe, at Chieng Sèn.

The only images that can be positively attributed to the founder of Chieng Mai are the terra cotta figures that originally stood in the niches at the Cetiya Sî Liem, which was built around 1300 (page 121). They are of exactly the same type as at Wat Kūkuṭa: the founder, we may guess, depended chiefly on Lampûn for religious art. Lampûn remained the cultural capital; its sculptors taught the Tai. A great many terra cottas and a certain number of bronzes might be attributed to the Tai kingdom of Lân Nâ in the 14th century; but in fact there is no way of distinguishing them from those produced previously in the independent kingdom of Lampûn.

There are reasons to believe that around 1370, under the inspiration of the Thera Sumana and other monks from Sukhodaya, this style was succeeded by a provincial version of the Sukhodaya style, which we may call the *style of the Thera Sumana*. It is admittedly hypothetical, for no dated images are known from this period: the only sure examples are sealed up inside the base of a shrine built about sixty years ago at Lampûn (Wat Pra Yün), where we cannot get at them. I am in-clined to attribute to the style of Sumana a large bronze statue which tradition

fig. 104 assigns – incorrectly, I think – to the founder of Chieng Mai. It looks like the work of inexperienced sculptors struggling with the complexities of the Sukhodaya walk-ing Buddha and the supernatural anatomy. As with the *Victorious King*, ortho-doxy has imposed equal length on the four fingers of each hand. The excessive length of the left arm, one of the 32 marks of the Buddha's person, is awkwardly rendered, and the walking position is poorly realized.

It is hard to say whether the style of the Thera Sumana accomplished anything better under the pious kings who reigned in the last quarter of the 14th century.

---

* See Dr. R. S. leMay's *Buddhist Art in Siam*, Cambridge, 1938, chapter VIII, and his *Culture of South-East Asia*, London, 1954, chapters X and XI, both written before my views appeared; for a summing-up, see his *Chronology of Northern Siamese Buddha Images*, Oriental Art, Spring, 1955, and his review of my book in The Middle Way, August, 1957. For a vigorous defense of the *early Chieng Sèn* chronology, see M. C. Chand and Khien Yimsiri, *Thai Monumental Bronzes*, Bangkok, 1957. For a fuller discussion of my views, see my *Buddha Images of Northern Siam*, JSS XLI/2, and my *Dated Buddha Images of Northern Siam*, Ascona, 1959; also Mr. Boisselier's review of my book in Artibus Asiae, XXI, 3/4, page 299 ff., and Mr. Sullivan's remarks on page 307 ff. of the same issue; also Mr. Cœdès in Arts Asiatiques, II/4, page 287.

During the long reign of the heretical king in the first half of the 15th the demand for expensive images could hardly have been very great. When he was deposed in 1441 the sculptural tradition was perhaps in danger of running out altogether.

In 1449 his successor, Tiloka, captured the city of Nân, where a competent school of image-makers carried on the Sukhodaya tradition; we have seen examples of the work they were doing 23 years earlier (page 123). Tiloka celebrated his victory by ordering them to see how quickly they could cast a huge Buddha image. As they completed the work in less than a hundred days, it would be uncharitable to judge it as severely as we might otherwise feel inclined to. *fig. 105*

A decade later Tiloka conquered Svargaloka, where the Sukhodaya tradition was deep-rooted and the love of sculpture amounted to a passion. In those days the capture of skilled craftsmen was one of the main motives for waging war, so we may be sure he rounded up as many of them as he could and sent them back to his capital. Among them, incidentally, were potters: it appears that from about this period the production of Svargaloka ware ceased at Svargaloka itself and began in Lân Nâ. The sculptors, both from Nân and from Svargaloka, would mingle with others who had been trained by an earlier generation at Chieng Mai. From about 1480 on, dated images of *mixed type* of a conventional sort begin to appear in Lân Nâ, more or less in the Sukhodaya post-classic manner, and doubtless some of the undated ones are a little earlier. Over a period of years the production of this sort of image grew enormous. The greatest masterpiece was completed in 1492, *fig. 106* five years after Tiloka's death. The example in our Exhibition appears to date *fig. 101* from the early 16 century.

Among the mixed types are a good many images wearing the Royal attire; the example in our Exhibition is one of the finest I have ever seen. I should date it *fig. 102* around 1500. As a general rule the jewels are superimposed on the monastic robe; but in this case if the *parure* were eliminated the body would be nude from the waist up, just as it sometimes was in the school of Lopburî.

Another work of considerable charm, though lacking the refinement of the two last-mentioned, is a statuette cast in 1482. Clearly its author had a Sukhodaya figure *fig. 111* in mind, for he has imitated the little hooks at the lower corners of the robe – but in such a way that they could hardly be mistaken for the hallmark of Sukhodaya workmanship (see page 94). Unlike the walking Buddhas of Sukhodaya, this one performs no gesture, but is intent on stamping the impression of his footsole in the same place where the three previous Buddhas of the present age had left their own footprints. Legend asserts that the first of them was nearly 70 feet tall, and the others progressively smaller, while the historical Buddha was a mere 30. In illustrating the footprints on the pedestal, the sculptor has respected the proportions.

As to the *lion type,* I believe it was introduced at the same time the Seven Spires Monastery was built. That structure, as we have seen, is a copy of the Mahābodhi temple at Bodhgayā and bears the same name (page 122). In like manner, the *Lion Lord* and the rest of the lion series must be copies of the *Lion of the Śākyas,* the famous Buddha image that occupied the place of honor at Bodhgayā. If Tiloka sent a mission to Bodhgayā to get the plans of the temple, as I believe he did, they would hardly fail to bring back with them a replica of the statue. (Another one seems to have been introduced at Sukhodaya at about the same time; see page 95.) Perhaps the replica was no more than a terra cotta tablet; or perhaps it was one of those black-stone reliefs, carved in the Pāla period, of which so many have been *fig. 107* found in the temple precinct at Bodhgayā. In any case the Indian style would be unfamiliar to the Chieng Mai sculptors; and when they copied it in their own idiom they created, in effect, a new style. The point is best illustrated by the earli- *fig. 108* est of the dated lion type images, which was cast in 1470. Judging from the dated examples, the images of this type in northern Siam were mostly produced between 1470 and 1525, with a single revival in 1565, and a bigger revival in the 19th and 20th centuries.

fig. 109   Of the two lion type images in our Exhibition, one is dated in 1486; the other, *fig. 100* which is undated, I should place a decade or two later. The plastic treatment, in- deed, is rather different, but no more so than in a good many dated examples; and it appears to be due more to the individual differences between two artists than to *fig. 110* any great difference in date. There is also a fragment, which may have belonged to a lion type image; I should give it about the same dating. Adherents of the Chieng Sèn theory say the dated image is of inferior workmanship, but deem the other to be much more beautiful and therefore earlier by 200 years or more. The reader (having duly noted that the rather unpleasant stare of the dated figure is the result of modern inlay in the eyes) may form his own opinion as to the relative merits of the two pieces, and decide for himself whether so subjective a test can provide a re- liable chronology.

An attractive kneeling figure in the Exhibition is probably an idealized por- *fig. 112* trait of a donor. I suspect it dates from the second half of the 15th century; the *fig. 113* round chignon and the diadem are very much like those of an Ayudhyā bronze of the same period.

Though Lân Nâ in general had an overwhelming preference for bronze, one locality, Payao, produced some very accomplished stone sculpture. None of it is dated, but the 16th century would be a good guess, as some comparable material, found in a case in Laos, is inscribed with a date equivalent to 1556, and some in- *cat. no. 18* scriptions of slightly earlier date have been discovered among the ruins of Payao.

Above: 95. The Seven Spires Monastery, near Chieng Mai.

96. Small stone model of the Mahābodhi Temple, Bodhgayā. Philadelphia Museum of Art. *(Photograph by courtesy of the Museum.)*

98. Stucco relief. Seven Spires
Monastery, near Chieng Mai.

99. Stucco relief. Seven Spires
Monastery, near Chieng Mai.

100. Seated Buddha. Bronze; ht. 58.5 cm. (Cat. no. 81.)

101. Seated Buddha. Bronze; ht. 68 cm. (Cat. no. 84.)

102. Crowned Buddha. Bronze; ht. 46.5 cm. (Cat. no. 85.)

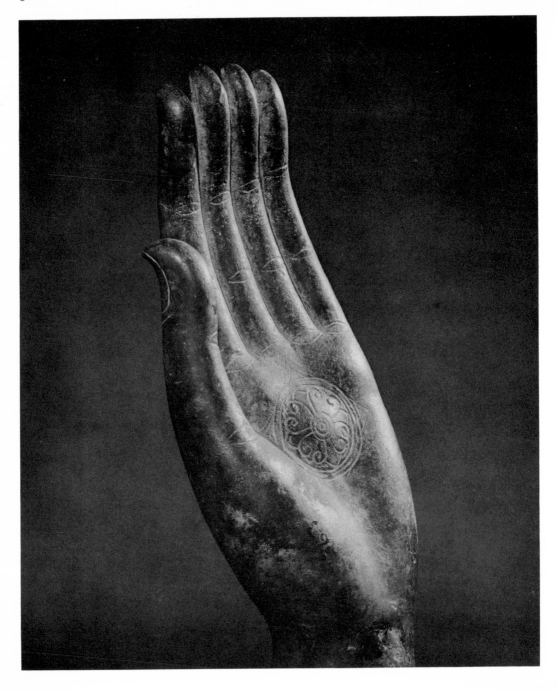

104. Standing Buddha. Bronze; ht. about
4.50 m. Kālakot Monastery, Chieng Mai.

105. Seated Buddha. Cast in 1449. Bronze; ht.
4.11 m. Monastery of the Sugar-Palm Grove,
Nan.

106. Seated Buddha. Cast in 1492. Bronze; ht.
2.35 m. Monastery of the Lion Lord (Wat Pra
Sing), Chieng Mai.

107. Small stone replica of the image called *Lion of the Śākyas*. From Bodhgayā. Philadelphia Museum of Art. *(Photograph by courtesy of the Museum.)*

108. Seated Buddha. Cast in 1470. Bronze; ht. 1.33 m. Kālakot Monastery, Chieng Mai.

109. Seated Buddha. Cast in 1486. Bronze; ht. 63 cm. (Cat. no. 82.)

110. Head of a Buddha image. Bronze; ht. 20 cm. (Cat. no. 86.)

111. The Buddha stamping the impression of his Footsole on the ground. Cast in 1482. Bronze; ht. 46 cm. (Cat. no. 83.)

112. Kneeling prince. Bronze; ht. 31.5 cm. (Cat. no. 87.)

113. Seated princess. Bronze; ht. 42 cm. Private collection, France.

114. Crown. Gold with
precious stones; ht. 13 cm.
(Cat. no. 138.)

115. Plate. Glazed ceramic;
diam. 23 cm. (Cat. no. 214.)

6. Û Tòng, Ayudhyā, and the National Style

IN 1350 the Prince of Û Tòng founded Ayudhyā, which became the strongest and most prosperous kingdom in the Southeast Asia Peninsula. Around 1430 its armies invaded Cambodia and captured Angkor, but retired soon after. A few years later Sukhodaya, long since reduced to vassalage, was incorporated into the kingdom. The city of Ayudhyā, it is estimated, had a larger population than London in the 16th century. Its rulers thought of themselves as the inheritors of both the Tai tradition of Sukhodaya and the Khmer tradition of Angkor. Though they were Theravāda Buddhists and gave generously to religion, they also honored the Brahmins and took over the Hindu ceremonial of the Angkorian Court.

In 1767 Ayudhyā was captured by the Burmese and stripped of its treasures. During the disorders the city caught fire and burnt to the ground.

⚇ Architecture ⚇

THE MOST CHARACTERISTIC and splendid form of monument is the *prāṅg*. It preserves the old concept of the Khmer temple-mountain, stylized and modified. One of the finest examples is Wat Rājapūraṇa, founded in 1424. The crypt inside it was recently opened, disclosing some rich mural painting and a large deposit of images and jewelry.

figs. 117 and 118

figs. 132-136

The design of the Ayudhyā *prāṅg* remained sturdy and majestic until the latter part of the 17th century, but after that it began to grow attenuated, springing from a slender pyramidal base which looks like a structure of superimposed Chinese tables. Again, a light *prāṅg* placed on the roof of a timber building had no structural significance: we might suppose it was merely "decorative" if we did not know that it was a badge of royalty.

The bell-shaped stupa perpetuates the traditions of Sukhodaya and Ceylon. Now and then the stucco trim, recalling the glories of Pagán, suggests Mòn workmanship. Often false-bays are added to the stupa base. Sometimes it is surrounded by rather Khmer-looking lions.

fig. 119

fig. 116

Another form of stupa, bell-shaped in outline, but square with deeply recessed angles in plan, vaguely recalls the curvilinear obelisk (*śikhara*) of Mòn temples like the Ananda at Pagán, but with the terraces and details smoothed away as if the architect had been inspired by some small and eroded replica. Often this type, which was a great favorite, was placed on top of a "Chinese-table" pyramidal base.

fig. 120

One of the most interesting monasteries is the Jayavardhanārāma, built by a king who reigned from 1630 to 1655. The *prāṅg* is firmly designed, and hardly to be distinguished from earlier models. Some fragments of walls have false-windows ornamented with delightful balusters of brickwork. Several of the towers in this complex are of a rather puzzling shape: perhaps they can be explained as a modification of the Mòn type of Wat Kūkuṭa (page 41), with its corners eaten away by a system of re-entrants. At the same time they recall, though not very distinctly, a type of Khmer monument seen at Bakong and Lolei; perhaps that is what the builder had in mind, for it is said that he had reconquered Cambodia and liked to imitate its architecture for his own glory.

figs. 121, 122

The assembly-halls and ordination-halls of monasteries continued the Sukhodaya tradition.

Van Vliet, in charge of the Dutch East India Company's affairs at Ayudhyā from 1629 to 1634, gives us a lively description of the "temples" (he means assembly-halls) in the monasteries:

Their appearance is often more beautiful than that of churches in Europe, only they are dark as no glass is used. The roofs are covered with red tiles, some with planks and lead. In the town and neighborhood there are 400 beautiful temples, adorned with many gilded towers and pyramids. Under the seats of the idols in some temples, big treasures of gold and silver have been buried, also many rubies, precious stones and other jewels have been put away in the highest tops of some towers and pyramids and these things remain there forever for the service of the gods. The houses and monasteries of the monks are built all around the temples. Usually they are made of wood. The front and back are ingeniously and expensively decorated with panels and relief work, the inside and outside are beautifully gilded and painted; the roof is covered with tiles; the corners are plastered with lime and are provided with nicely cut wooden decoration.

LaLoubère, Louis XIV's ambassador, was in Ayudhyā in 1678 and 1688. I quote from his *Historical Relation of the Kingdom of Siam,* "done out of French" and published in London in 1693:

They know no exterior Ornament for Palaces, nor for Temples, save in the Roofs. As for what concerns the five Orders of Architecture, composed of Columns, Architraves, Frizes, and other Ornaments, the *Siameses* have not any knowledge thereof. That which amongst them makes the real dignity of the Royal Houses and the Temples, is that altho there is no more than one story, yet they are not all level. The Roofs are all high-ridged, but the one is lower than the other; as it covers a part lower than another. And a lower Roof seems to come out from a higher Roof, and the highest to bear on the lowest, like a Saddle, the fore-bow of which bears on the hind-part of another.

The overlapping roofs are indeed the glory of Siamese architecture, as any visitor to Bangkok knows. They must have been much the same in Ayudhyā times. A good example, though somewhat restored, can be seen in a building at Lopburî, originally erected for the Persian Ambassador, later converted into a Muslim *fig. 121* mosque, and finally into a Buddhist ordination-hall.

❦ *Sculpture* ❧

IT IS THE CUSTOM to classify under the name *Ū Tòng* a very numerous category of bronze Buddhas. Though it was recognized that most of them might be more correctly termed "early Ayudhyā," some of them might be pre-Ayudhyā; so the less specific appellation was chosen. They combine Mòn, Khmer and Tai ingredients in varying proportions. If we wish to sub-divide them, we can call those that most resemble Dvāravatī Group A, those with Khmer-looking faces Group B, and those with oval faces Group C.

The dates of the three groups, which no doubt overlapped to some extent, are uncertain. For reasons with which I will not burden the reader, and which in any event are not conclusive, I feel that the *terminus a quo* given in our Catalogue is in each case about a hundred years too early. For Group A, some of which are per- *fig. 124* haps really pre-Ayudhyā, I should say 13th and 14th centuries, but hardly 12th. I suppose Group B belong to the earliest style of Ayudhyā, say 1350-1425, but prob- *fig. 125* ably not 13th century. I should put Group C next, say 1400-1475, but I think not *fig. 123* in the 14th century.

A deposit of images recently discovered in the crypt of Wat Rajapūraṇa would tend to corroborate these guesses. The monument, according to the Annals, was founded in 1424; we do not know how many years it took to finish, but the deposit would be placed in the crypt when it was nearing completion. A few of the images found in the deposit are obviously much older than the monument; as to the rest, it is reasonable to assume that those found in the greatest quantity were almost new at the time they were deposited, while those found in lesser but still large quantity were a little older. There were two or three dozen examples of Group B, and several hundred of Group C.

Ayudhyā was the main center of production, though "Ū Tòng" bronzes were also made in Cambodia and at Sukhodaya, doubtless the work of craftsmen imitating models provided by the suzerain power. In any case, they are of a very different character from Khmer classic statuary, and even more remote from the Sukhodaya high classic. In general they are marked by a sort of soldierly dignity, particularly Group B, with their square Khmer-looking jaws and uncompromising expression. Group C owe more to Sukhodaya, but convey little sense of spiritual fervor; the modeling is firm rather than fluent. A good example of the style, said to have been dug up in the ruins of Lopburî, bears an inscription in Mòn, unfortunately not dated but attributable to the 15th century on the grounds of spelling and script. Group C images were produced in enormous quantity. The bronze-casters developed great dexterity in making the metal go as far as possible, often using so little wax in preparing for the casting that the metal is no more than a paper-thin skin over the baked clay core.

Most Westerners find it easy to appreciate the Ū Tòng bronzes. The human anatomy, though stylized and simplified, is far less amended by supernatural considerations than at Sukhodaya. The forms are strong and decisive, though frequently softened by a richly-variegated patina which it is worthwhile to examine under a powerful glass.

A large group of stone Buddhas are very similar to the Ū Tòng B and C bronzes. In spite of this, when I wrote about them several years ago, historical considerations prompted me to date them in the 17th century. I was wrong; and Dr. R. S. leMay, who had previously attributed an earlier date to them, was right. Now, since two examples were discovered in the Wat Rājapūraṇa crypt, we can safely date them with their bronze counterparts. If we want to go on calling the bronzes Ū Tòng — and it would be difficult to change so firmly-established a custom — we should call the stone figures Ū Tòng too. Two detached heads in the Exhibition give an idea of the style. One of them corresponds to Ū Tòng B, say 1350-1425; the other corresponds to Ū Tòng C, say 1400-1475.

The finds at Wat Rājapūraṇa included some delightful miniature sculpture in gold; logic suggests that it too should be classified as Ū Tòng.

Around the middle of the 15th century the Ū Tòng style began to merge into the "ordinary Ayudhyā" or National Style. We can sense the transition in the series of Jātaka figures cast in 1458. We are fortunate in having two superb heads

fig. 125

fig. 123

cat. no. 19
cat. no. 20

fig. 134

fig. 127

from this series in our Exhibition. The treatment of eyes and eyebrows in one of them recalls a variety of Ŭ Tòng Buddhas associated with the Subarṇapurī region; in the other it evokes the National Style.

One of the most charming works of Ayudhyā art is a bronze statuette of a princess, perhaps cast to illustrate the Court costume prescribed in the Palatine Law *fig. 113* for princesses of a certain grade; I should date it, like its male counterpart from *fig. 112* Chieng Mai, in the second half of the 15th century.

Ayuthyā made some beautiful stucco work, but most of it was destroyed when the city was burned, or by treasure-hunters afterwards. A fine example, of uncertain date, still remains at Wat Lai, in the province of Lopburî.

The National Style lasted for more than 300 years, and ended badly. Mass production was its downfall: the image-makers, I suppose, forgot how to use the sort of memory-picture that could give life to "copying," and became content with mere copying in the western sense. Some of their best work is in figures of the Buddha wearing the royal attire; but it is the attire, rather than the Buddha, that counts.

116. Bell-shaped stupa, Ayudhyā.

117. *Prāṅg* of Wat Rājapūraṇa, Ayudhyā.

Opposite above: 119. Ruins of the Monastery of the Omniscient Lord (Śrī Sarbejña) , Ayudhyā.

Opposite below: 120. Ruins of the Jayavardhanārāma, Ayudhyā.

Below: 118. *Prāṅg* of Wat Rāja-pūraṇa, Ayudhyā. (a) Longitudinal section and cross section. (b) Elevation and exterior half-plan.

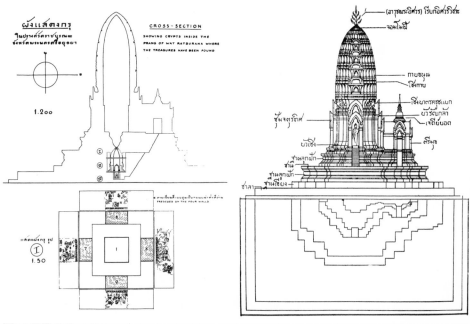

Above: 121. The Golden Flagpole Monastery, Lopburî.

122. Model of a *vihāra*. Wood; ht. 61 cm. (Cat. no. 227.)

123. Seated Buddha. Bronze; ht. about 30 cm.
Private collection, Lopburî.

124. Seated Buddha. Bronze; ht. 49 cm. (Cat. no. 88.)

125. Seated Buddha. Bronze; ht. 46 cm. (Cat. no. 89.)

126. Standing Buddha. Wood; ht. 99 cm. (Cat. no. 224.)

127. Head of a *jātaka* figure (hermit). Bronze fragment;
ht. 22.5 cm. (Cat. no. 99.)

128. Hermit. Bronze; ht. 20 cm. (Cat. no. 101.)

129. Three demons. Bronze; ht. 13.5 cm. (Cat. no. 102.)

Above: 130. Lock and key. Bronze; length 15 cm. (Cat. no. 129.)

131. Bo tree. Stone; ht. 48 cm. (Cat. no. 21.)

133. Plaque in the form of a swan. Gold;
ht. 5.8 cm. (Cat. no. 149.)

134. Guardian figure. Gold; ht. 10 cm.
(Cat. no. 139.)

135. Wrist band. Gold with precious stones; ht. 5.5 cm.; diam. 8.8 cm. (Cat. no. 159.)

136. Pair of bird divinities. Gold relief on bezel of a ring; diam. 1.8 cm. (Cat. no. 161.)

137. Pentachromatic bowl. Porcelain; ht. 8 cm. (Cat. no. 218.)

7. Tonburî and Bangkok

THE SIAMESE did not attempt to rebuild the old capital; instead they established a new one farther down the river at Bangkok. At first it was on the right bank, at Tonburî, but in 1782 it was transferred to the present site of Bangkok, on the left bank.

ⓖ *Architecture* ⓖ

THE BUILDERS of Bangkok wanted to make it as much like Ayudhyā as possible. Ayudhyā was an island, so a canal was dug to complete the watery circuit around the new site. An immense amount of building had to be done, but there was no need to introduce new architectural forms, as monasteries and palaces reproduced the remembered glories of the past.

After a time, however, Chinese architecture became popular in Bangkok. A little later, imitations of European buildings began to appear, or rather imitations of the neo-classic colonial buildings of places like Singapore, sometimes modified into an easy-going *chinoiserie*. The intrusion was at first pleasant enough, and even the late Victorian domestic achitecture in Bangkok is comfortable and picturesque. In the 20th century, however, the intrusion of western and Chinese styles, hideously transformed, has gotten out of control. Fortunately there are still plenty of old houses left in the less fashionable sections: their teak paneling and up-leaping bargeboards are a joy to look at.

Monasteries. The Siamese monumental style, as manifested in the first hundred years of the Bangkok period, is a marvel of grace and fantasy. Architectural forms grow more exuberant without in the least losing their elegant coherency. Often, to catch the light and enchant the eye, surfaces of wall and stupa are faced with porcelain tiles or inlaid with bits of chinaware in floral patterns. The *prāṅg*, taller and lighter than ever, is still held aloft by the mythical inhabitants of Mount Meru's slopes. The most usual type of stupa, as in the latter days of Ayudhyā, is the curvilinear obelisk with recessed angles.

fig. 138

The bell-shaped stupas are strong and solid in design: one of the most impressive monuments in the world is Braḥ Paṭhama, over 375 feet in height, its surface covered with brilliantly-glazed orange-yellow tile. Completed in the early years of the present century, it "encases" an older monument, which is itself probably com-

fig. 139

posed of several successive encasements, the innermost core dating from the Dvāra-vatī period or even earlier.

The assembly-hall and ordination-hall carry on the traditions of Ayudhyā and Sukhodaya. The characteristic type, built of brick coated with white stucco, is a long nave with side-aisles, with or without a peristyle, and surmounted by a flight *fig. 140* of overlapping roofs tiled in patterns of dazzling color. Stylized *nāgas* of carved and gilded wood writhe down the gable-eaves, brandishing their combined tails at the top and rearing their cobra-heads at the lower corners. Usually the gable-end contains a composition in carved wood representing Śiva mounted on a bull, Vishṇu on a *garuda,* or some other heritage of Angkorian Hinduism placed at the service of the Buddha. Doors and windows are surmounted by miniature mountain-systems with *nāgas* and flames, the lesser peaks of Mount Meru charged with fiery energy. The portals and window-shutters are wood, carved, lacquered in black and gold, or painted, or inlaid with mother-of-pearl, depicting guardian divinities or scenes of enchanted forests or still-lifes of fruit and flowers. Stairway-balustrades take the form of *nāgas,* the rainbows that are the ladders to heaven. The entrance is usually at the east end of the nave. Inside, the main Buddha image stands or sits near the west end, facing the entrance, and sometimes the interior walls are covered with painted scenes.

Monastery libraries are like miniature assembly-halls, often built on stilts in a pond so as to prevent termites from getting in.

As to the *maṇḍapa,* one of the finest examples is the shelter over the Buddha's *fig. 141* Footprint at Srapurī. The square building has a peristyle of porcelain-faced columns supporting the roof, which is a pyramid with false-dormers and *nāgas* on its seven tiers.

Shrines sometimes take the form of a *prāsāda* or palace, of cruciform plan, with a *prāṅg* placed on top at the intersection of the roofs. The presence of palace architecture in a monastery is not incongruous: it commemorates the ancient custom of Buddhist monarchs who converted their own residences to monasteries and presented them to religion. A beautiful combination of such distinctive forms can be seen in the silhouette of the Chapel Royal (vulgarly called the Temple of the Emerald Buddha).

The Jetavanārāma in Bangkok (Wat Pó, the *Bo-Tree Monastery)* was begun by King Rāma I (1782-1806) and greatly enlarged by King Rāma III (1824-1851). The latter wished it to be an encyclopedia of all the traditional knowledge and science, secular as well as religious; he caused long inscriptions to be made for those who could read, and paintings for those who could not, dealing with the life of the Buddha and his disciples, astronomy and astrology, geography and the races of

men, mythology, poetry and medicine. The main quadrangle, with its soaring ordination-hall, is enclosed in a majestic gallery which intersects a chapel at each of the cardinal points; and outside it, radiating like the segments of a *maṇḍala*, lesser galleries enclose small garden-courtyards that invite meditation. Around and about stand tall glistening stupas and miniature mountains of tree-clad rocks. In the western precinct there are more stupas and miniature mountains, a pond, a library, pavilions and school-rooms, and the hall of the immense reclining Buddha. This figure, larger than an American railroad car, is a deeply moving work, though one can hardly judge it as sculpture: the hall, though vast, is too small for the beholder to stand far enough away to see the image as a whole. The footsoles, inlaid with
fig. 90   the 108 auspicious signs in mother-of-pearl, are like huge tablets bearing a message of good omen.

Monasteries of the most spectacular beauty are too numerous to list, much less to illustrate; but I cannot refrain from mentioning a few of my favorites: Rājapra-tishṭa, Rājapabita, Sudarśana, and Pavaranivesa, all in Bangkok; and Chlöm Braḥ Kirti, on the right bank of the river a few miles upstream, in the rustic shade of ancient trees.

fig. 142   *Palace architecture.* The Grand Palace at Bangkok, containing buildings of every period from the foundation of the city to modern times, is a happy blend of European and Siamese forms. A no less happy blend of European and Chinese forms can be seen in King Mongkut's palace at Bejrapurī, built in the 1860's. As to the Siamese style proper, fine examples are fortunately numerous. One, built in the late 18th century, is the Buddhaiśvarya Building in the old palace of the Wang Nâ Prince, now the National Museum. Another, built at the beginning of the
fig. 143   present century, is a delightful water-pavilion.

The Golden Meru. Architecturally rendered, the artificial mountain is an in-exhaustible theme, applicable to stupas, to the designs of palace and monastery buildings, to door and window trim, to elephant-howdahs and barge pavilions. One of its most splendid manifestations, the funeral pyre of royalty, popularly called the *Golden Meru*, is beautifully depicted on a panel in the Lacquer Pavilion
fig. 144   at Suan Pakkad Palace.

⑥ *Sculpture* ⑨

fig. 145   THE BANGKOK SCULPTORS excelled in miniature figures. They put plenty of
fig. 146   vigor into the Brahmanical gods riding their chosen animals, and into the animals themselves; they put pathos into the episodes from the Buddha's life; and they put a real sense of terror into their evocations of hell. They were admirable carvers of

bas-relief as well: their scenes from epic poetry are composed with *brio,* and executed with assurance.

They were less successful in making images of the Buddha. One of the most curious series was cast in the reign of King Rāma III, in an attempt to standardize the iconography. It includes a number of new postures invented *ad hoc* to represent specific episodes, and attaches specific meanings to the old ones. Most of the new postures were quickly forgotten, though one survived to the reign of King Rāma V. Nor have the rules about the old postures been very strictly observed. Especially in painting, the iconography does not need to be stereotyped so long as the meaning is clear.*

In the early days of Bangkok the need to restore the glories of the past, which gave such an impetus to architecture, had the opposite effect on image-making. The most pressing need was to "take pity on the old images of the Lord that lay neglected among the ruins, exposed to sun and rain." In the popular mind they were living beings: it would have been both unkind and wasteful not to rescue them and put them back in working order so as to fulfill their protective function. At the command of King Rāma I, more than 1200 bronze Buddha images, of life size or larger, were gathered up at Ayudhyā, Sukhodaya and elsewhere, brought to Bangkok, and installed in monasteries. For some time, therefore, the supply of large Buddha images was sufficient, and there was little or no demand for new ones. When the demand at length revived, it was too late: competence could be regained, but not inspiration.

As to the old images that King Rāma I assembled, those that were not required as cult images in monasteries were set up in the Jetavanārāma, ranged symmetrically in the different cloisters. For some reason they were all *encased* in a thick coating of plaster before being gilded, and thus converted in appearance into spiritless and absolutely uniform copies of one another. A few years ago the monastery authorities began removing the plaster encasement, and revealed a number of sublime masterpieces of richly-patinated bronze. Piety quickly hid them again, though not so completely, by giving them a coat of lacquer and gold leaf, so that the dazzled eye cannot appreciate their sculptural quality. Yet this must have been their original appearance: according to the old belief, the Buddha's skin was the *color of gold,* and the rays of his fiery energy were so intense that his true form could only be seen by means of prolonged meditation.

---

*Cf. Cat. no. 248, a painting in which the Buddha, in the upper register, is obviously preaching, though his hands are in the position of *meditation;* and in the lower, though he is descending from heaven, he has the right hand up and the left hand down, instead of performing the gesture of *exposition* with both hands according to the rules.

Above: 138.   Monastery of the Dawn, Tonburî.

139. Stupa of Braḥ Paṭhama Monastery, Nagara Pathama.

Above: 140. Great Relic Monastery, Nagara Śrī Dharmarāja.

141. *Maṇḍapa* at the shrine of the Buddha's Footprint, Srapurī.

Above: 142. Grand Palace, Bangkok.

143. Pavilion in a pond, Bâng Pa In.

144. The Buddha's funeral pyre, in the form of a Golden Meru. From a panel in the Lacquer Pavilion, Suan Pakkad Palace, Bangkok. *(By gracious permission of H.R.H. Princess Chumbhot of Nagara Svarga.)*

145. Ceremonial utensil. Gilt brass; ht. 44.2 cm.
(Cat. no. 131.)

146. Episodes from the Buddha's life. Bronze; ht. 13.5 cm.
(Cat. no. 104.)

147. The goddess of the Earth wringing the water from her
hair. Bronze; ht. 38.5 cm. (Cat. no. 107.)

148. Episode from the *Rāmakirti*. Marble relief; 45.5 cm. x 45.5 cm. (Cat. no. 24.)

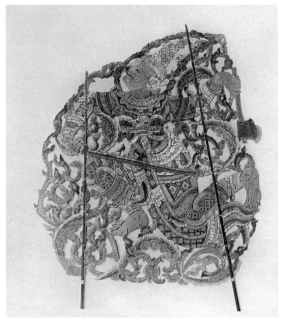

149. Shadow-play figure. Leather; ht. 145 cm. (Cat. no. 269.)

150. Mask of Lakshmana. Papier-mâché; ht. 68 cm.
(Cat. no. 277.)

151. Food receptacle. Wood inlaid with
mother-of-pearl; ht. 57 cm.
(Cat. no. 282.)

152. Covered bowl. Silver; ht. 54 cm.
(Cat. no. 176.)

Below: 153. Bowl. Niello ware; diam.
21 cm. (Cat. no. 171.)

A Note on Thai Painting

by ELIZABETH LYONS

THE PAINTING OF Thailand is an art of great interest as well as of remarkable beauty. It is also almost completely unknown to the western world. This surprising obscurity is due to a combination of geography, climate, time, and, unintentionally, to the Thai themselves. To the western eye the most striking paintings are the murals done between the 17th century and about 1820 on monastery walls. Only two good examples of this period exist in Bangkok, but neither is mentioned in the usual guidebooks. Most tourists find the hot and humid climate extremely enervating and rarely venture very far from the routine tour. The climate, too, has destroyed all but a few isolated specimens of anything earlier than the 17th century and has ruined much of what is left of later examples. As the majority of Thai regard the paintings from a religious viewpoint rather than an aesthetic one, they do not believe a non-Buddhist would be interested, and they politely do not call them to the foreigner's attention.

The basic purpose of the paintings, like the paintings of medieval Christian Europe, is to instruct, guide, and inspire the devout by portraying scenes of religious history. In both worlds, the artist was an anonymous monk or dedicated layman whose aim was to teach and elucidate a sacred text. In many a monastery the walls are painted with more devotion than skill, but often the painter was also blessed with a great natural talent, and then his creations are stirring by any standard.

There are several different forms of painting. The most important are the murals which may be found in one or more of the buildings which make up the wat complex. Many of these have vanished in the last few decades, but typically a hall would have its walls covered with murals from a shoulder-high dado to the dim reaches of the high ceiling. The top part of the wall facing the main Buddha image is generally painted with a representation of the unsuccessful temptation and attack by Māra, an allegory of the victory over evil. Behind the image will be scenes of Hell. The life of Buddha or *Jātaka* stories are pictured on the other two walls. They are often surmounted by rows of seated Buddhas or heavenly beings.

figs. 160 and 161

Another type of painting in the possession of a wat may be long cloth banners which are displayed on special occasions. The most usual form shows a standing *fig. 154* figure of the Buddha flanked by two disciples or attendants. Also seen, but more rarely, are the main events of his life, such as the Great Departure, the Preaching in the Deer Park, or the Death. Not many paintings on cloth earlier than the 18th century have survived, and most are of the 19th, but the evidence of a few seems to show that in the pre-Bangkok period large panels containing several scenes from the life of Buddha were more popular than single incidents. There are also a few rare instances of such scenes painted on wood.

Probably every wat once also owned a set of scenes on cloth or *kòi* paper illustrating the *Jātaka* story of Prince Vessantara. The Buddhist countries of Southeast Asia seem to choose for frequent illustration those *Jātakas* among the 547 which portray the virtues, such as perseverance, austerity, or self-sacrifice, that they regard as most representative of their own national characteristics. The overwhelming favorite with the Thai is the history of Prince Vessantara, who was renowned for *cf. fig. 161* great selfless generosity. It is, today, one of the first stories a child learns to read.

The Thai version, which differs only in a few unimportant details from the original Pali, is usually recited in 13 chapters of verse, and the majority of the painted sets contain 13 scenes, painted by one artist. The quality of these sets differs greatly, from naive and primitive to very skillful.

Paintings on cloth or paper parallel the style and development of the mural paintings although they do not often match them in quality. Perhaps this statement is true only for the Bangkok period as the few surviving Ayudhyā examples are extremely fine.

One large cloth panel, measuring about four and a half feet by seven must date in comparison with the Bejrapurī murals as late 17th or early 18th century. The subject is the life of Buddha. The composition is an interesting pattern of irregularly placed episodes separated from each other by zigzag fences of striated lines. The drawing is as precise and delicate as in the finest murals and the color is soft and clear. Prince Siddartha is making his final departure from the palace and everyone is sound asleep, except for one grubby servant who is peering into the kitchen pots to see if anything is left for a midnight snack.

The largest number of cloth panels are those on which are portrayed the standing Buddha and two disciples. These are difficult to date as they are often traditional and mechanical repetitions and it is easy to confuse the provincial with the primitive. Few or perhaps none date earlier than the Bangkok period.

The most interesting of the panels are the *Vessantarajātaka* sets. Although none of this type seems to have survived the fall of Ayudhyā they must go back much earlier.

These sets figured in a popular tradition that was kept up until the early part of this century. It was a custom for the eldest son of a prominent family during some period of his monastic service to return home for a religious celebration. For his part in the ceremony he would recite the Vessantara story, using the paintings from his wat as illustrations.

Definite regional differences can be seen in these sets. No doubt there was a wat in each district which trained artists. Wat Yai in Bejrapurī was one of these and it still has a collection of the last four generations of pupils. In an article of this length one can only give a few general characteristics of the different regions. Those of the Ayudhyā district are often delicate and use a great deal of gold leaf. Rājapurī examples show the most sophisticated compositions. Bejrapurī is the most traditional and has the widest range in quality. Chieng Mai has the most freedom of interpretation and the appeal of good folk art. The few examples from Nagara Śrī Dharmarāja in the far south show an odd light color tonality on an almost white background.

Manuscript illustrations represent an important category of painting. The long, narrow, palm leaf books, like the Indian ones, have had a continual use in Thailand, but are rarely illustrated. The usual illustrated manuscript, called a *samut dhātu* is of *kòi* paper in one continuous sheet folded like an accordion. It is read across the length of the page. Those of pre-Bangkok date usually have a *figs. 156* large illustration in the middle of the page, sometimes covering the double un-*and 157* folded section. Those of later date generally have one or two smaller illustrations on the ends of the page with the text between them.

Murals, paintings on cloth, and manuscripts represent the largest part and the most important aspects of Thai painting. The other examples play a subsidiary role although to class them merely as "decorative" is rather arbitrary. This is especially true of the guardian figures generally painted on the inner side of the doors and window shutters of monastery buildings. Usually not painted by the muralist, they are often stock types, but they are usually graceful and benign figures, quite unlike their fierce Chinese and Japanese comrades-in-arms who guard the Buddhist world from harm. In a few wat buildings, the window shutters have still lifes of *fig. 158* offerings, flowers, bowls of fruit or rice. These are done in quite a different style from the murals; in fact, with their strong patterns and flat color they seem to foreshadow modern western art. According to the monks, they were painted by Chinese artists who were also employed for decorative bits on columns or beams.

Designs in gold leaf on black lacquer, found particularly on large wooden book-

cases, chests and on screens are still another type of pictorial art worthy of notice.* *figs. 159 and 163*
The usual subjects of the life of Buddha or *Jātaka* scenes may be illustrated, but
legendary themes or designs of plants or animals are even more likely to appear.
One of the most effective uses of this technique in architectural decoration occurs
in an early 18th century monastery library, now restored in the grounds of Suan
Pakkad Palace in Bangkok. With its numerous panels depicting, in the upper registers, the principal events in the life of the Buddha, and in the lower registers, *fig. 144*
scenes from the Rāmakirti, this unique jewel-like structure represents the high
point of graphic art of the Ayudhyā period. It is also an invaluable document of
the life of the Kingdom of Ayudhyā at the moment of its greatest prosperity.

The covered galleries in the courtyard of the Chapel Royal (the so-called Temple of the Emerald Buddha) in Bangkok contain on their walls a long series of
frescoes devoted to the Rāmakirti, which is the Thai version of the Rāmāyaṇa. The
nationalization of the great Hindu epic affords opportunities for the depiction of
scenes of Thai history as well as of the mythological subject. In the north, particularly in Chieng Mai, there was also a tendency towards the realistic and even earthy
representation of everyday scenes, especially with regard to the common folk, as
distinguished from the formal style used for royal or divine activities.

The style of Thai painting has the basic elements of all Asian painting. There
is no western perspective which uses a fixed view and a vanishing point on the hori-
zon. Here, the spectator is allowed to rove through the painting. He may look down
into a courtyard, or stand directly before an audience hall, and perhaps both at
the same time if the illusion of distance is achieved by the relative placement of
the figures and objects and by overlapping.

The composition is a combination of mass and line. The figures are drawn with
an even, flowing contour, then filled in with flat color and the detail and ornament

---

* Lacquer design which reached its zenith in the 18th century in Ayudhyā has a technique which
requires thorough experience. It consists in applying on the wooden panel three coats of black
lacquer (the juice of a plant growing in the north of Thailand); afterwards the surface is smoothed
and over it a drawing is traced. All parts which have to remain black are painted with a gummy
yellow paint and once this is dry a very thin coat of lacquer is painted all over the panel; while
this lacquer is still not quite dry, gold leaf is applied all over the surface. After twenty hours the
work is washed with water which carries away the gold leaf adhering to the gummy paint. The
design appears as neat as ink-drawing. This kind of technique is termed *lâi rot nâm*, which means
ornament emerging by washing the work with water.

There is a great similarity in the composition of regular paintings and of lacquer painting. The
difference between the two arts is that in painting the artist may leave large spaces without detailed figures such as mountains, water or sky, while the design for lacquer must fill up all the
spaces with evenly distributed masses; if the dark and light values are not well distributed the
result is disharmonious.

applied. This is identical with the Indian and early Islamic technique. Buildings, furniture, chariots, and other elements are done in the same way, but the background is a generalized landscape. Here and there a group of rocks or a clump of flowers shows Chinese influence in the style. The artist has probably copied and adapted these bits from porcelain or decorative screens. He does not consider landscape as important in itself; it is only the necessary incidental setting for the action. In some cases the contrast between an uninspired or crude background and the sensitive, intricate figures leads one to believe that the former was done by pupils or lesser artists.

In the narrative murals there is a type of continuous action, although the scenes do not merge into each other. The important episodes are separated in the early examples by an arbitrary zig-zag line, and usually by more naturalistic means such as a row of trees, a wall, or a screen in the later periods.

The technique of the paintings has a few unusual points. For murals, the wall is prepared by washing it several times with water in which *kî-lek* leaves *(Cassia siamea leguminosaea)* have been pounded. This is supposed to remove any traces of salt. Then a coating of plaster, white chalk mixed with a binder of tamarind seeds which have been baked, ground and boiled, is applied and carefully smoothed. Cloth and paper are sized with a thin application of the same mixture. It adheres quite well to cotton, but unfortunately flakes off silk and becomes powdery on paper.

The paints are mineral and earth pigments like malachite and cinnabar; from the beginning of the 18th century, at least, they have been imported from China in powder form. The duller and more limited colors of the earliest paintings are probably local pigments as is the red ochre always used for a preliminary outline. The binder used with the paints is a tree gum, *ma-kwit (Feronia elephantum rutaceae)*. Another gum, *ma-düa (Ficus hispida urticaceae)*, is used as a glue for the gold leaf. The paint is applied to the dry plaster; thus it is not a true fresco technique.

Brushes are made of tree roots and bark and are often set into elaborate silver handles. The brush of *lam-jiek* root *(Pandanus tectorius)* is cut flat across the end and then split several times. This produces a stippling effect which is used for trees and shrubbery masses. Another brush is made of *gradang-ngâ (Canagium odoratum)* bark which peels off in long flakes. The ends of this are pounded and frayed. Both brushes are well soaked in water to make them pliable before using. Details are added with brushes made of cow's hair, and exceptionally fine work may be done with a special brush made of hair taken from the inner part of a cow's ear.

Much of the distinctive appearance of Thai painting is due to those wooden brushes. They give an even, wire-like line, often of amazing sinuosity, and quite unlike the modeling line of the flexible Chinese brush.

It is unfortunate that Thailand adopted a type of dry fresco which is much too perishable in a humid climate. Only a few examples remain which can be safely dated before the 17th century, yet historical references and archeology give evidence that painting must have existed much earlier.

Dvāravatī, the kingdom of the Mòn in central Thailand, undoubtedly had connections with India of the Gupta period (see page 40). It is reasonable to expect that an Indian tradition of painting, such as may be seen at Ajanta in India or Sigirīya in Ceylon, would also be implanted in Thailand, but we have only a few bits of rather crudely incised stone to show the relationship. The Dvāravatī paintings were probably similar to those done by their cousins, the western Mòn of Burma, at Pagán around the 12th century.

There is no trace of any painting surviving from the Lopburî period. In the 14th century we are on the trail of actual painting. Set into the ceiling of a narrow stairway at Wat Sî Chum, Sukhodaya, are several stone slabs incised with *Jātaka* *fig. 68* scenes and identifying inscriptions in the Sukhodaya script. The linear style of the illustrations and the detailed representation of jewelry and ornament are certainly derived from manuscript painting, but it is difficult to trace the original source.

A building at the "Seven Rows of Reminders," Svargaloka, has a few faded fragments of murals of the Sukhodaya period still clinging to its walls, but the first fairly well preserved painting is found at Wat Rajapūraṇa in Ayudhyā, founded in 1424. The paintings are in a crypt which remained sealed from the date of its construction until recently.

The paintings are of two types: there are hieratic rows of seated Buddhas and standing disciples, and illustrations from *Jātaka* stories. An interesting note is the ceiling decoration of a large circular medallion formed with concentric bands and floral zones, and surrounded with small gilt circles. A similar medallion is found on an Ajanta ceiling. There is also a frieze of heavenly beings closely related to the style of the Sukhodaya stone engravings. On two walls of this crypt are Chinese scenes too fragmentary for positive identification but unmistakably Chinese in content and execution. In spite of long contact with China and a rather large Chinese population, very little Chinese influence shows on Thai painting, and there are only rare examples of actual Chinese work.

Manuscripts of the Ayudhyā period provide important help in dating paintings besides being interesting in their own right. One of the most treasured manuscripts in the National Museum collection is a *Traibhūmi*, a mid-sixteenth century copy of a 14th century treatise on Buddhist cosmology. It is an unusually large one, unfolding to a length of about five feet. The illustrations include ten of the *Jātakas* and the thirteen chapters of the Vessantara story.

While not technically of the finest quality, this manuscript is an important document to show the continuity and slow development of Thai painting. For example, the figures of gods and goddesses in the Himavanta forest go back in stylistic conception through the Sukhodaya stone engravings to the Ajanta type, and as they go forward from the 16th century to the 19th century painting they suffer only minor changes in their coiffure and costume and grow a little more lissom.

Also present in the manuscript are the stylized landscape forms and the groups of neatly detailed plants and flowers which seem to be derived from Chinese porcelain. The floral ornament was present earlier, but not in as naturalistic a style.

fig. 160   The paintings in Wat Yai, Bejrapurī, considered from historical evidence to have been done around 1650, show rows of seated and praying heavenly beings, including Indra and Brahmā. The figures are not small in scale, each row measuring over two feet in height, but the technique is delicate and miniaturistic and the ornament is detailed. Each figure is given a certain measure of isolation and importance by having its head and shoulders framed in a tent-shaped space. The edges of the tent are marked with vertical striations with a curious hook at the top of each line. The general effect is of a flowered and fringed baldachin with triangular apertures hanging over the figures. That may indeed have been the original source of the motif. These striations are mentioned because they are an element in the dating of other paintings. They occur again in the murals of Wat Go in Bejrapurī, finished in 1714. Here the usage is similar, but in other 18th century work the hooked striations are used like a picket fence to separate one scene from another.

fig. 161   From the fall of Ayudhyā to the middle of the 19th century the paintings grow in richness of color heightened by a lavish use of gold leaf, and in complexity of composition. The figures are extremely graceful. The heavenly or earthly palaces with their glittering, soaring spires and their multicolored and many-layered roofs have the splendor of fantasy although they have substantial and only slightly more prosaic counterparts in the wats of Bangkok. Richly dressed processions of men and elephants wind through the hills to bring Prince Vessantara back from exile. Crows gather to listen to the teaching of the Buddha. Armies of the Buddhist world, including clearly depicted Indians, Chinese, and Japanese, fight for his relics after his death, and are defeated by a Portuguese honor guard. The Buddhaiśvarya Chapel in the National Museum Compound, Bangkok, Wat Tushita and Wat Suvarṇārāma in Tonburî, and Wat Sudarśana ("Wat Sutat") in Bangkok have the finest examples of this rich and colorful style.

The painting of Northern Thailand is strongly Burmese in style. There is nothing that predates the 19th century. The drawing of the northern murals is somewhat less sensitive and graceful and the color is much colder in tone. The effect is dry, crisp and much less luxurious than that of the Bangkok school.

Wat Pra Sing, in Chieng Mai (early 19th century), is perhaps the most important of these northern wats. One of the walls is painted with the story of Pra Sâng Tòng, a fairy story prince who was born in a golden conch shell. This is one of the "Fifty Stories" that are often represented in place of the authentic *Jātakas* in this area. In the Wat Pra Sing mural, the royal personages are clothed in traditional Thai costume, the traditional one which survives today in the dance. The courtiers and the common people are dressed in contemporary Burmese style. There is a great deal of factual reporting and earthy humor: a man flirts with a group of girls and on the roof above his head one cat stalks another. Other paintings, rich in scenes of local life, are found at Wat Bhūmindra in Nân, east of Chieng Mai, and in Payao. *frontis-piece*

In Thailand painting, like sculpture, architecture and the dance, was in the service of religion from its earliest days, and still is to a large extent. Thailand enriched the simple ritual of Buddhism by borrowing themes from the Hindus and Brahmins as well as certain rites concerning artists. The painter dedicated his life to his craft, and thereby to the service of the Buddha. He went through an ordination, part of which is similar to the ordination of a monk, being dressed in white and presenting traditional objects of sacrifice.

The villagers have also accepted the Indian traditions regarding the painter's attitude towards his art. They say that the painter must not take his craft lightly, that he must pay respect to his teacher, that he must go through the proper ceremonies and explain to the spirits that when he paints the life of Buddha it is an act of devotion and not the usurping of creation or the imitation of holy events. They also say that a painter will usually paint only one set of pictures and that he will leave one section unfinished because when he adds the last stroke his life's work will be done and he will die. The truth of this is hard to check, but it explains such puzzling conventions as a broken roof line or a missing column, in so many of the Vessantara sets.

Traditional Thai painting began to die out in Bangkok in the middle of the 19th century. Western oil paints were introduced and the artist found a new interest in Western shading and perspective and occasionally in Western scenes. The result was something akin to *chinoiserie,* often pleasing and decorative; but this is essentially a hybrid growth.

The Śilpākara (Fine Arts) School in Bangkok has trained some painters in the old techniques and they have preserved in copies some of the vanishing murals. Traditional painting, however, actually survives only in a few villages. The young artist in the cities has joined the modern, international, art movement and is finding new ways to express his long and rich heritage.

154. Standing Buddha. Painting on cloth; ht. 305 cm. (Cat. no. 243.)

155. The return to Kapilavastu. Painting on wood; Ht. 100.5 cm. (Cat. no. 251.)

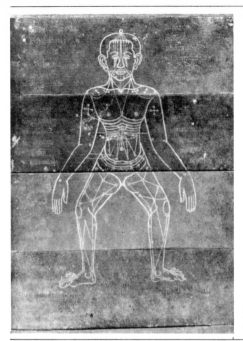

156. Illustration in a manuscript on massage. Paper; total length of manuscript when unfolded, 6.44 m.; width, 35 cm. (Cat. no. 262.)

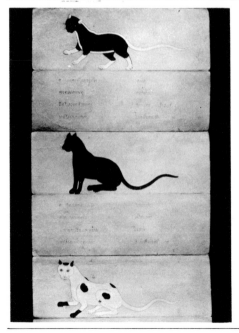

157. Illustration in a manuscript on cats and birds. Paper; total length of manuscript when unfolded, 9.20 m.; width, 36 cm. (Cat. no. 263.)

a gift to the Buddhist religion. The dress and jewelry of this figure are typically Thai.

88. *Buddha* *(fig. 124)*
Bronze. H. 49 cm.
National Museum, Bangkok
From the town of Singhapuri
Ū Tòng style, group "A." 12th-13th century
Cf. pp. 141-2

89. *Buddha* *(fig. 125)*
Bronze. H. 46 cm.
National Museum, Bangkok
From the town of Gampèng Pet
Ū Tòng style, group "B." 13th-14th century

90. *Buddha*
Bronze. H. 51 cm.
National Museum, Bangkok
Ū Tòng style, group "B." 13th-14th century

91. *Head of a Buddha Image*
Bronze. H. 27 cm.
National Museum, Bangkok
Ū Tòng style, group "B." 13th-14th century

92. *Buddha*
Bronze. H. 54.5 cm.
National Museum, Ayudhyā. Found in the crypt of Wat Rājapūraṇa, Ayudhyā
Ū Tòng style, group "C." 14th-15th century

93. *Buddha*
Gilt bronze. H. 98 cm.
Monastery of the Fifth King
(Peñcamapabitra), Bangkok
Ayudhyā style. 17th-18th century

Buddha wearing the attire of Royalty superimposed over the monastic robe. During the Ayudhyā period, such figures were believed to represent the apocryphal story of the *Buddha frightening Jambutati.* (p. 73)

94. *Buddha* *(fig. 76)*
Bronze. H. 187 cm.
Monastery of the Fifth King
(Peñcamapabitra), Bangkok

Ayudhyā style, 15th-16th century

This is one of the finest surviving images of the Ayudhyā period. Judging by the facial features and the form of the crown, we might suppose that it was the creation of a late Sukhodaya sculptor, or at least of a sculptor trained in the Sukhodaya tradition.

95. *Buddha*
Bronze. H. 60 cm.
Monastery of the Fifth King
(Peñcamapabitra), Bangkok
Ayudhyā style, school of
Nagara Śrī Dharmarāja. 16th-18th century
Other examples of the same series have been published in JSS XXXVIII/2.

During the Ayudhyā period Nagara Śrī Dharmarāja produced a numerous series of images which are more or less free copies of the most famous image in that city, the *Buddha Sihiṅga.* Their iconography is like the early Chieng Sèn (lion) type.

96. *Head of a Buddha Image*
Bronze. H. 35 cm.
National Museum, Lopburî
Ayudhyā style, 16th-17th century

97. *Disciple*
Bronze. H. 13.5 cm.
National Museum, Ayudhyā. Discovered in a stupa at the Monastery of the Omniscient One (Śrī Sarbejña), Ayudhyā
Ayudhyā style. Late 15th century

Seated figure performing the gesture of respect *(añjali).* This figure was intended as an accessory to a Buddha image. It can be dated by the fact that it was discovered in a stupa whose approximate date is known.

98. *Disciple*
Bronze. H. 26 cm.
National Museum, Ayudhyā. Discovered in a stupa at the Monastery of the Omniscient One, Ayudhyā
Ayudhyā style. Late 15th century

Standing figure performing the gesture of respect.

99. *Head* *(fig. 127)*
Bronze. H. 22.5 cm.
National Museum, Bangkok. Discovered in the Monastery of the Omniscient One, Ayudhyā
Ayudhyā style. 1458 A. D.

Head of a hermit. It is practically certain that this was one of the figures cast by King Paramatrailokanātha in 1458 to illustrate the 550 *Jākatas* (previous lives of the Buddha) .

100. *Head*
Bronze. H. 22.5 cm.
National Museum, Bangkok. Discovered in the Monastery of the Omniscient One, Ayudhyā
Ayudhyā style. 1458 A. D.

Another of the same series of *Jātaka* figures.

101. *Hermit Kneeling* *(fig. 128)*
Bronze. H. 20 cm.
National Museum, Bangkok
Ayudhyā style. 17th-18th century

Figure of a bearded hermit *(rishi)*, probably intended for use in a Brahmin ceremony.

102. *Fragment of a Pedestal* *(fig. 129)*
Bronze. H. 13.5 cm.
National Museum, Bangkok
Ayudhyā style. 17th-18th century

The pedestal doubtless supported a figure of the Buddha in the attitude of victory over Māra. The demons shown here are members of Māra's armies at the moment of their defeat.

103. *The Severance of the Hairlock*
Bronze. H. 5.5 cm. L. 9.2 cm.
National Museum, Bangkok
Bangkok style. Mid-19th century

One of a series of episodes from the life of the Buddha, cast by command of King Rāma III (1824-1851) . The future Buddha severs his long hair with his sword in token of his renunciation of his high caste in order to become a wandering ascetic. His groom and his horse bid him a sorrowful farewell. The god Brahmā offers him a set of monastic garments, and another divinity offers him an almsbowl, while Indra holds a tray to receive the Hairlock Relic.

104. *Episodes Following the Enlightenment* *(fig. 146)*
Bronze. H. 13.5 cm.; L. 10.5 cm.
Bangkok style. Mid-19th century

One of a series representing episodes from the life of the Buddha. On the left, the Buddha gazing in gratitude at the Bo tree. In the center he meditates while walking on a miraculously-created path in the sky, touching the sun and the moon with his hands. On the right he sits in the miraculously-created "house of gems," meditating on the Metaphysics.

105. *Buddha*
Brass. H. 73.5 cm.
National Museum, Bangkok
Bangkok style. Late 19th century

This work was cast by command of King Rāma V (1868-1910) (King Chulalongkorn) to illustrate the Gandhāran style of sculpture, as being the originator of the anthropomorphic Buddha image. While the designs on the balustrade imitate Gandhāran motifs, the naturalistic anatomy of the Buddha figure suggests western influence. The attitude, newly invented during the Bangkok period, signifies "calling down rain."

106. *Pra Mâlai Visiting Hell*
Bronze. H. (including pedestal) 88 cm.
National Museum, Nagara Paṭhama
Bangkok style. 19th-20th century
Published: Artibus Asiae, xx/1, fig. 7.

The Story *of Pra Mâlai* is a popular cautionary poem composed in the 18th century. The monk Pra Mâlai visits hell, and later heaven, to inquire about the punishments and rewards that are consequent on various acts. Here he is seen preaching to the sufferers in hell. Some have animal heads, another has his face on his stomach, and so on, according to the evil deeds they committed while on earth. Their attitudes of misery contrast with the serene demeanor of the monk. His monastic robe is draped in the Bangkok fashion, and decorated with designs; his alms-bowl is slung to his right shoulder, and he held a monastic hand-screen which is now lost.

107. *The Earth-Goddess Wringing Water from her Hair* *(fig. 147)*
Bronze. H. 38.5 cm.
National Museum, Bangkok
Bangkok style. First half of 19th century

While meditating under the Bo tree in order to gain Enlightenment, the future Buddha was taunted by the Lord of Evil, who demanded to know what acts of merit he had performed in past lives that would entitle him to achieve his goal. The future Buddha, who had indeed performed a huge quantity of such acts and *poured water* (cf. no. 249) upon the earth each time in the Hindu ceremony of recording a legal act, did not reply; instead, he moved his right hand to his knee and pointed downwards, calling the Earth to witness. At that moment the Goddess of Earth appeared, her hair drenched with the water of record; and when she wrung it out, the ensuing flood put the armies of the Lord of Evil to flight. The story is accepted by Buddhists as an allegory, signifying that in order to attain Enlightenment it is necessary to have performed a long series of meritorious deeds in past lives.

IV. Objects in Bronze, Brass and Lead

(108 — 136)

108. *Hand of a Buddha Image*
Bronze. H. 24.5 cm.
National Museum, Bangkok
From Svargaloka
Lopburî style. 13th-14th century

Right hand, performing the gesture of exposition, probably from a standing figure representing the Descent from Heaven. Inscribed in the palm is a Wheel of the Doctrine, the symbol of the First Sermon and (by extension) of preaching in general.

109. *Reliquary* *(fig. 43)*
Bronze. H. 23 cm.
National Museum, Bangkok
Lopburî style. 13th-14th century

Miniature octagonal shrine of Khmer-Thai design, supported by atlantes in the form of lions, and containing Buddha images in niches, surmounted by a stupa of Sinhalese form. It was probably used to contain relics of the Buddha or ashes of the deceased.

110. *Ceremonial Utensil* *(fig. 44)*
Bronze. H. 42 cm.
National Museum, Bangkok
Lopburî style. 11th-12th century
Published: BK, Pl. XXXIX and page 51.

This object may be part of a ceremonial chariot or a bow; Coedès describes it as a candle-holder used in the ceremony of *wientien* ("passing candles around in a circle"). The principal figure is Vajrasattva, the Buddha particularly worshiped by the Mahāyānist Vajrayāna sect: he was considered to be the active agent of Adibuddha, the primordial intelligence that governs the universe. Vajrasattva, holding a double *vajra* (thunderbolt) in his right hand and a bell (?) in his left, sits on a pedestal supported by lions.

Above his head is the Adibuddha seated on the coiled body of the *nāga*. At the end of the handle there is the mask of a monster (*kāla*).

111. *Pair of Lions*
Bronze. H. 25 cm.
National Museum, Bangkok
Lopburî style. 13th-14th century
   Doubtless used as door guardians.

112. *Part of a Frame for a Buddha Image*
Bronze. H. 20 cm.
National Museum, Bangkok
Lopburî style. 12th-13th century
Published: MNB, Pl. XXIV.

113. *Back-frame for an Image*   (*fig. 45*)
Bronze. H. 30.5 cm. W. 16 cm.
National Museum, Bangkok
Lopburî style. 13th-14th century
   Slab with eleven niches containing small Buddhas, and empty space in front for a standing Buddha image; bodhi tree in background. The images may represent several of the many different Buddhas worshiped in the *Mahāyāna*.

114. *Pedestal for a Buddha Image*   (*fig. 49*)
Bronze. H. 25.5 cm.
Collection of H. R. H.
Prince Bhanubandhu Yugala
Lopburî style. 12th-14th century
   This superb pedestal consists of an upper section with lion supporters and a lower section illustrating scenes from the Life of the Buddha and from the *Vessantarajātaka*; at the bottom of each side, a glory-face or *kāla*.

115. *Pedestal*   (*fig. 48*)
Bronze. H. 12 cm.
National Museum, Bangkok
From Subarṇapurī
Lopburî style. 11th-12th century
   Lion-atlantes and scenes from the *Rāmāyaṇa* (?): two standing male figures with two seated figures (hermit and heroine?); male figures with horse-drawn chariot.

116. *Four Fittings for a Palanquin*
Bronze.
National Museum, Bangkok. From the province of Kórât and elsewhere
Lopburî style. 12th-14th century
Similar pieces are illustrated and described in MNB, Pl. XXVI
   Bronzes originally attached to various parts of a wooden palanquin, as depicted in the bas-reliefs of the Bayon at Angkor.

117. *Six Fittings for a Chariot*   (*fig. 52*)
Bronze. H. of *Garuda*. 45 cm.
National Museum, Bangkok
Lopburî style. 13th-14th century
Similar pieces are published in BK, Pl. XLIV and MNB, Pl. XXV.
   Bronzes originally attached to various parts of a wooden chariot.

118. *Candlestick*
Bronze. H. 18 cm.
National Museum, Bangkok
From Purīramya
Lopburî style. 12th-14th century
   Lotus-stem issuing from the mouth of a *kāla* and terminating in the head of a bird. Perhaps the work of a Thai artist.

119. *Horn for a Bow*
Bronze. L. 73 cm.
National Museum, Bangkok
From Sukhodaya
Lopburî style. 13th-14th century
   Horn in the form of a *nāga*-head for a ceremonial bow, perhaps used for dipping into the water which was to be drunk by vassals and others when taking the oath of allegiance to the king.

120. *Vessel*
Bronze. H. 8.5 cm.
National Museum, Bangkok
Lopburî style. 12th-14th century
   Vessel for offerings, with *garudas* as supporters, and their mortal enemies, *nāgas*, as feet.

121. *Bowl*
Bronze. H. 10.5 cm.
National Museum, Bangkok
From Surāshtradhānī Province
Lopburî style. 11th-14th century

122. *Bell*
Bronze. H. 19 cm.
National Museum, Bangkok
Lopburî style. 12th-14th century
Similar bells are illustrated and described
in BK, Pls. XXXVII and XXXVIII and on page 51.

The handle is in the form of a *vajra*
(thunderbolt). Used in Tantric ceremonies.

123. *Elephant-Bell*
Bronze. H. 26 cm.
National Museum, Bangkok
From Chieng Mai Province
Lopburî style. 13th-15th century
A similar bell is illustrated in BK, Pl. XLV.

124. *Hand of a Buddha Image*   *(fig. 103)*
Bronze. H. 34 cm.
National Museum, Bangkok
Sukhodaya style. 14th century

The palm is inscribed with a floral design,
perhaps a stylized Wheel of the Doctrine.

125. *Miniature Shrine*
Bronze. H. 61.5 cm.
National Museum, Bangkok
From the town of Chieng Sèn
Chieng Sèn style. 15th-16th century
(Cf. page 122)

Octagonal shrine in the form of a *maṇḍapa*
designed to contain relics or an image of the
Buddha. The atlantes are alternating lions
and elephants; four door-guardians stand
between the four door-openings; and the roof
is decorated with false-dormers in the usual
Thai tradition inherited from India.

126. *Water-pot in the Form of a Swan*
Bronze. H. 20 cm. L. 30.7 cm.
National Museum, Bangkok
Chieng Sèn style. 15th-16th century

127. *Hands of a Buddha Image*
Bronze. L. 26 cm.
National Museum, Ayudhyā
Ayudhyā style. 16th-18th century

The Buddha was sitting in meditation,
with legs folded and both hands lying in his
lap.

128. *Urn*
Bronze. H. 78 cm.
National Museum, Bankok. Exhumed
from the ruins of a palace near the
Bodhārāma, Ayudhyā
Ayudhyā style. 17th-18th century

Container for the ashes of deceased royalty
before enshrining them permanently in a
stūpa. Doubtless a copy of the gilded wooden
urn that contained the body of the deceased
during the ceremonies that preceded the
cremation.

129. *Bronze Lock, with Key*   *(fig. 130)*
L. 15 cm.
National Museum, Bangkok. From the
shrine of the Buddha's Footprint
(Braḥ Buddhapāda), near Srapurī
Ayudhyā style. 17th-18th century

Lock in the form of the demon Rāhu
entwined with a serpent. The key can no
longer be removed from the lock.

130. *Bronze Bowl with Stand*
Diameter of bowl 18 cm.
National Museum, Bangkok
Ayudhyā style. 17th-18th century

Intended to hold lustral water during a
ceremony.

131. *Ceremonial Candle-holder*   *(fig. 145)*
Gilt brass. H. 44.2 cm.; W. 14.7 cm.
National Museum, Bangkok
Bangkok style. Mid-19th- early 20th century

The ceremony of passing lighted candles
around an object of worship or an object to
be blessed is of Hindu origin (cf. no. 110).
It is still practiced frequently in Thailand,
not only in Hindu ceremonies but also in a

Buddhist context. This candle-holder is one of a set depicting the gods of the nine planets. Here the god Angāra, regent of the planet Mars, rides his usual mount, the buffalo. The three rosettes above probably represent stars.

132. *Ceremonial Candle-holder*
Gilt brass. H. 44.2 cm.; W. 14.7 cm.
National Museum, Bangkok

See no. 131. Here the god Brihaspatī, regent of the planet Jupiter, rides his usual mount, the deer.

133. *Pair of* Garudas
Bronze. H. 16.5 and 14.7 cm.
National Museum, Bangkok
Bangkok style. Early 20th century

Garuda, king of birds and mount of Vishṇu, was adopted in the Bangkok period as the emblem of the King of Thailand and of the Thai nation.

134. *Swan* (haṁsa)
Bronze. H. 73 cm.
National Museum, Bangkok. Found in a canal in Aranyapradesha district, Prācīnapurī Province
Bangkok style. 19th-20th century

It is said that the Burmese King of Haṁsā-vatī (Pegu), who conquered Ayudhyā in the 16th century, commanded that a mast should be erected with a swan (haṁsa) on top at every monastery in Thailand in memory of his conquest. The conquest is an historical fact, and it is also a fact that such masts are to be seen at many monasteries; but the story, as explaining the origin of the custom, is very doubtful. Such bronze swans are also used on lamp-posts; that was probably the case with this one, which has a ring at the beak to suspend a lamp.

135. *Buddhist Votive Tablet* (*fig. 15*)
Gilt lead. H. 20 cm.
National Museum, Bangkok
Dvāravatī style, 6th-11th century
Cf. SVT, Pl. I.

This tablet represents the Mahābodhi shrine at Bodhgayā containing the famous image known as the Śakyāsiṁha, or "Lion of the Śākyas". It is inscribed with the so-called Buddhist credo ("*Ye dhamma....*") in Devanāgari characters. It was discovered in the stupa of Braḥ Śrī Sarbejña in Ayudhyā. It may have already been an antique when the stupa was built in the late 15th century, or was cast at that time from an antique mould.

136. *Votive Tablet*
Lead. H. 31.5 cm.
National Museum, Bangkok
From Subarṇapuri
Sukhodaya style. 14th-15th century
An identical tablet is published in SVT, Pl. XIII.

This tablet was discovered in the Great Relic Monastery, Subarṇapuri, of which the main prāṅg is thought to have been built by a king of Ayudhyā in the early 15th century. The double parasol at the top suggests that the image in the shrine represented the Buddha descending from heaven.

V. Gold, Jewelry, Niello and Silver Objects
(137 – 177)

137. *Crown*
Gold, studded with four small precious stones. H. 14.5 cm.
Wat Cetiya Luang, Chieng Mai
Chieng Sèn style. 15th-16th century

Exhumed inside the old *vihāra* south of the Cetiya Luang. Probably made to adorn the head of a Buddha image, and presented to the image by royalty as a mark of respect.

138. *Crown* (*fig. 114*)
Gold, studded with three small rubies.

H. 13 cm.

Wat Cetiya Luang, Chieng Mai

Chieng Sèn style. 15th-16th century

Exhumed inside the old *vihāra* south of the Cetiya Luang. See number 137. Note the scroll-work imitating the curled hair of the Buddha.

139-168. *Thirty objects from the Ayudhyā Treasure*

In the early 15th century two Thai princes who were brothers, fighting for the throne of Ayudhyā, killed each other in an elephant duel. The third brother therefore became king. He built a monastery with a large shrine in the form of a *prang* at the cremation-site of the deceased princes. The foundation-deposit, discovered in the crypt of Wat Rāja-pūraṇa, Ayudhyā (Cf. plate 117 and 118) contained the largest treasure ever found at Ayudhyā. Many of the articles comprising it must have belonged to the two deceased; others were offerings in honor of the relics of the Buddha which were enshrined above their ashes.

The objects on loan, constituting a small but representative fraction of the treasure, are all in the early 15th-century Ayudhyā style. The treasure belongs to the National Museum of that city, but until the new Ayudhyā museum building is completed, it will continue to be displayed in the National Museum in Bangkok.

139. *Guardian figure   (fig. 134)*
Gold. H. without pedestal, 10 cm.

This small figure, of Thai workmanship though its dress and earrings recall Khmer figures of an earlier date, was doubtless regarded as a protector of the royal treasure.

140. *Votive Plaque*
Gold. H. 28.8 cm.

Gold plaques cut or embossed into Buddha images were found inside many stupas and were probably put there as votive tablets. This large piece of gold is embossed with a figure of the standing Buddha *dispelling fear* He is decorated with ornaments showing the *Mahāyāna* influence, as can be seen from his belt and front part of the lower garment. The halo around the head ends in beautiful scrolls. The outer garment covers both shoulders.

141. *Votive Plaque*
Gold. H. 11 cm.

The Buddha, giving protection, stands under the Bodhi tree.

142. *Votive Plaque*
Gold. H. 8.1 cm.

143. *Votive Plaque*
Silver. H. 10.5 cm.

The walking Buddha is flanked by two disciples.

144. *Votive Plaque*
Silver. H. 9.4 cm.

145. *Votive Plaque*
Silver. H. 9.2 cm.

146. *Arch for a small shrine*
Gold. H. 17 cm.

This fragment of a small shrine in the form of an arch is in the typical Thai style, with some reminiscences of Khmer art.

147. *Votive Tablet   (fig. 132)*
Tin. H. 26.5 cm.

The walking Buddha is surrounded by fifty smaller Buddhas in the attitude of *calling the Earth to witness*. All the figures are in gold leaf on a bright red background.

148. *Plaque in the Form of a Deity*
Gold. H. 6 cm.

Thin pieces of gold, cut into various shapes, were traditionally enclosed as auspicious omens in the foundation stones of important edifices.

149. *Plaque in the Form of a Swan*   *(fig. 133)*
Gold H. 5.8 cm.

150. *Plaque in the Form of a Horse*
Gold. H. 6.7 cm.

151. *Plaque in the Form of a Mythical
Animal, half Horse and half Bird*
Gold. H. 6.4 cm.

152. *Plaque in the Form of an Elephant*
Gold. H. 8.8 cm.

153. *Plaque in the Form of a Mythical
Animal, half Elephant and half Bird*
Gold. H. 8.5 cm.

154. *Plaque in the Form of a Cow*
Gold. H. 9.5 cm.

155. *Seven Parts of a Jeweled Pendant*
Gold decorated with precious stones
The width of the pieces varies from
2.7 cm. to 4.8 cm.

The seven parts of this jewel may have
formed part of a larger group serving as a
chain for the jeweled plaque (No. 156).

156. *Pectoral Plaque*
Gold decorated with precious stones
11.5 x 9.2 cm.

157. *Jeweled Brooch*
Gold decorated with precious stones
6 x 4 cm.

The floral design is composed of a large
cat's eye surrounded by small green stones.
The borders are dotted with silver pebbles.

158. *Arm-band*
Gold decorated with precious stones
H. 13.5 cm., D. 3.5 cm.

159. *Wrist-band*   *(fig. 135)*
Gold decorated with precious stones
H. 5.5 cm., D. 8.8 cm.

160. *Bracelet*
Gold decorated with rubies and other
precious stones. H. 1.3 cm., D. 7.5 cm.

Similar bracelets were sometimes used to
adorn a top-knot on a child's head.

161. *Ring*   *(fig. 136)*
Gold. D. 1.8 cm.

This heavy ring, probably belonging to a
royal personage, has a carved design of two
intertwined *kinnara*.

162. *Ring*
Gold. D. 1.8 cm.

A floral design forms the ornamentation
of this ring.

163. *Ring*
Gold decorated with rubies. D. 2.5 cm.

This ring is in the form of a coiled snake.

164. *Ring*
Gold decorated with precious stones
D. 1.7 cm.

165. *A Bunch of Betel-nuts*
Gold. L. 9 cm.

166. *Octagonal Box*
Gold H. 3.2 cm., W. 4.8 cm.

This box, decorated with bird and floral
motifs, was probably used as part of a betel-
nut set. (Cf. No. 173)

167. *Round Box with a Lid*
Gold. H. 5 cm., D. 6.5 cm.

The lid is decorated with lotus and scroll
motifs, and the box was probably part of a
betel-nut set.

168. *Receptacle*
Gold. H. 9 cm.

This receptacle was probably part of a
betel-nut set.

---

169. *The Buddha Taming the Elephant Nalagiri*
Gilt lead. H. 10.5 cm.
Ayudhyā style. Late 15th century A. D.

National Museum, Bangkok. Found in the
Monastery of the Omniscient One, Ayudhyā.

170. *Box in the form of a Lion*
Gold set with jewels
H. 5.3 cm., length 6.5 cm.
National Museum, Ayudhyā. Found in a
prāṅg at the Great Relic Monastery
(Mahādhātu) , Ayudhyā
Ayudhyā style. Late 14th century

Chinese type of lion, but probably made
by a Thai artist. The upper part of the body
is the lid of the box. The animal's ears and
tongue are movable. This box probably
contained objects of value, and was buried
inside the stupa as an offering to the relics
of the Buddha.

171. *Bowl*   *(fig. 153)*
Gilt niello on silver. H. 10.5 cm., D. 21 cm.
Collection of Prince Piyarangsit Rangsit,
Bangkok
Bangkok style. 19th century

The niello technique was introduced during the Ayudhyā period, perhaps from China.
Much of the best niello-ware was produced
at Nagara Śrī Dharmarāja. This bowl was
probably intended for lustral water in a
ceremony. The animals of the 12-year cycle
are depicted on it: rat, ox, tiger, hare, *nāga*,
serpent, goat, horse, monkey, cock, dog, and
boar. This type of design, in which the gilt
figures leave much of the black background
visible, indicates a relatively early date.

172. *Bowl*
Gilt niello on silver. H. 9.8 cm., D. 18.8 cm.
Collection of Prince Piyarangsit Rangsit,
Bangkok
Bangkok style. 19th century

Each medallion contains the figure of a
garuda grasping a pair of *nāgas* by the tail.

173. *Betel-nut set*
Gilt niello on silver; tops of lids inset
with jewels. H. 24 cm.
Collection of Prince Piyarangsit Rangsit,
Bangkok
Bangkok style. 19th century

Tray with containers for the ingredients
in betel-chewing: "betel-nuts" (really seeds
of the palm-tree *areca catechu*), leaves of the
betel vine *(piper betle)* , tobacco, lime, etc.

174. *Water-pot*
Gilt niello on silver. H. 24 cm.
Collection of Prince Piyaransit Rangsit
Bangkok style. Late 19th century

The over-all design in gilt, leaving much
less of the black background showing than
in nos. 171 and 172, indicates a later date.

175. *Bowl and Stand*
Gilt niello on silver
H. 10.7 cm. Diameter of bowl 28.4 cm.
National Museum, Bangkok
Bangkok style. Late 19th century

Bowl to contain water for drinking or
washing the face.

176. *Covered Bowl*   *(fig. 152)*
Silver. H. with lid, 54 cm., D. 42 cm.
National Museum, Bangkok
Bangkok style. Late 19th or 20th century

Container for food at ceremonies or ban-
quets. The lotus petals each frame a little
creature, divinities on the lid and the bowl,
and demons on the base.

177. *Three inscribed Plaques*
Gilt silver
Lengths 20 cm., 25.4 cm., and 28.4 cm.
respectively
National Museum, Lampûn
Chieng Sèn style. 20th century

Dedicated by pious persons to the Great
Reliquary at Lampûn. Animal figures on the
plaques represent the cyclical years in which
the donors were born.

(1) Upper register: *nāga*, ox, *nāga*; lower
register: *nāga*, ox, *nāga*. Inscription recording the donors' wish to attain Nirvana.

(2) Upper register: elephant, horse, ox,
goat, rabbit; lower register: cock, horse, tiger,
monkey, goat. Inscriptions as in (1) .

(3) Monkey, elephant, horse, ox, rabbit,

goat, rat. The inscription, with a date equivalent to 1914 A. D., records a pilgrimage of five persons from Chieng Mai to worship at Lampûn.

VI. Ceramics
(178 — 223)

SIAMESE CERAMICS fall into three major groups:
1) Lopburî wares created between the 11th and the 14th centuries, and showing strong Cambodian influence.

2) The wares of Sukhodaya and its twin city Svargaloka (Swankalók), made in the kingdom of Sukhodaya in the 14th century and the first half of the 15th century, with techniques introduced by Chinese potters. The decorated glazed stonewares of Sukhodaya resemble products of the Tzu-ch'ou kilns, while the glazed stonewares and monochrome celadons of Swankalók resemble those of Luang-ch'üan.

The presence of large numbers of Siamese ceramics in Southeast Asia, particularly Indonesia and the Philippine Islands, has been taken to mean that they were made especially for the export trade during the golden age of Sukhodaya. (Cf. Charles Nelson Spinks, *Siamese Pottery in Indonesia*, Bangkok, 1959.)

3) Chieng Mai wares, very likely introduced by potters from Swankalók who were taken as prisoners of war to Northern Siam in the middle of the 15th century. This production seems to have continued for about 100 years.

Apart from these three groups of Siamese wares, mention must be made of the Chinese export wares designed for the Siamese market in the 18th and 19th centuries. Until the 18th century most Siamese ceramics have monochromatic glazes with white, green, gray-green and brown tones predominating, while the imports from China have polychromatic decorations under a colorless glaze. Unglazed works are specifically noted.

178-183. *Examples of the Lopburi style, 11th to 14th centuries*

178. *Jar* *(fig. 59)*
H. 53 cm.
National Museum, Bangkok
Other examples are illustrated in MNB, Pl. XXVIII
    Partially covered with brown glaze.

179. *Pot in the Form of an Elephant*
H. 17 cm.
National Museum, Ayudhyā. From Lopburî

180. *Pot in the Form of a Rabbit with silver lid*
H. 12 cm.
National Museum, Bangkok

181. *Spouted Pot*
H. of the body, 8.5 cm.
National Museum, Ayudhyā. From Lopburî

182. *Spouted Pot in the Form of a Toad*   *(fig. 60)*
H. 12 cm.
National Museum, Ayudhyā

183. *Covered Jar*   *(fig. 61)*
Terra cotta. H. 15 cm.
Collection of Mr. James H. W. Thompson, Bangkok
    This unglazed jar, with its dark brown paint, its triangular striations and the bird forms on its body, is one of the handsomest Lopburî vessels in existence.

184-209. *Examples of Sukhodaya and Swankalók wares, 14th-15th centuries*

184. *Three Maternity Dolls*   *(fig. 91)*
H. 11.5, 10.5, and 10 cm. respectively
National Museum, Bangkok
    The heads of the figurines of nursing mothers were broken off in order to ward off evil spirits.

185. *A Hunchback*   *(fig. 92)*
H. 15.3 cm.
National Museum, Bangkok

186. *Building Ornament*   *(fig. 70)*
H. 61 cm.
National Museum, Bangkok
    The heads of *Nāgas* as well as of demons

and lions were used in religious architecture as protective omens.

187. *A Demon Head* *(fig. 71)*
H. 17.5 cm.
National Museum, Bangkok

188. *Elephant and Riders*
H. 23.5 cm.
National Museum, Bangkok
These elaborate statuettes served both decorative and ritualistic purposes. The riders and outriders of this war or ceremonial elephant are missing.

189. *Covered Bowl*
H. 16.5 cm., D. 17 cm.
Collection of H. R. H.
Prince Bhanubandhu Yugala, Bangkok
The bowl, with black designs on a white ground, is in the shape of a persimmon. The handle on the lid is stylized, however, and not in the usual imitation of the stem of the fruit.

190. *Covered Bowl*
H. 20 cm., D. 19 cm.
National Museum, Bangkok

191. *White Covered Jar*
H. 23 cm.
National Museum, Bangkok
Jars with a white, unadorned glaze, are relatively rare.

192. *Green Covered Jar*
H. 41 cm.
National Museum, Bangkok

193. *Brown Covered Jar with Four Handles*
H. 14.5 cm.

194. *Green Bowl*
H. 13.5 cm.
National Museum, Bangkok
Collection of H. R. H.
Prince Bhanubandhu Yugala, Bangkok

195. *Mortar Bowl*
H. 13.4 cm., D. 20 cm.
National Museum, Bangkok
Swankalók mortar bowls, with dark designs on a white ground, are relatively rare.

196. *White Water-bottle*
H. 16.5 cm.
Collection of H. R. H.
Prince Bhanubandhu Yugala, Bangkok
Such ewers, also known as *kèndi* or *narghili*, often have animal or bird forms.

197. *Green Water-bottle*
H. 16.5 cm.
National Museum, Bangkok

198. *Water-bottle in the Form of a Swan (fig. 93)*
H. 21.5 cm.
National Museum, Bangkok
The base and the tail have been restored.

199. *Jar*
H. 22 cm.
National Museum, Bangkok
The cup rim around the neck was presumably made to hold water as a protection against insects.

200. *Fluted Jar*
H. 23 cm.
Collection of H. R. H.
Prince Bhanubandhu Yugala, Bangkok

201. *Small Jar*
H. 12 cm.
National Museum, Bangkok
The brown glaze stops evenly two-thirds of the way down.

202. *Small Jar*
H. 11 cm.
National Museum, Bangkok
This has the same form as No. 201, but with a full greenish glaze and concentric lines around its neck.

203. *Platter*
D. 43.5 cm.
Collection of Prince Bhanubandhu Yugala, Bangkok

This flawless platter of Svargaloka celadon, with its underglaze ornaments of fish and abstract motifs, is one of the largest in existence.

204. *Large Bowl*
D. 28 cm.
National Museum, Ayudhyā

An example of a mixture of crackled green glaze and designs suggestive of the lotus leaf and flower.

205. *Flower Vase*
H. 24.5 cm.
National Museum, Bangkok

With its ten ridges and its light greenish glaze, this vase is a relatively rare specimen.

206. *Vase*
H. 20.5 cm.
National Museum, Bangkok

Green glaze over neck and body, which are partly crackled and partly decorated with underglaze leaf pattern.

207. *Vase*
H. 22 cm.
National Museum, Bangkok

This glazed vase with black designs on a white ground is in the Tzu-ch'ou style.

208. *Kiln Waster*
H. 23.5 cm.
Collection of H. R. H. Princess Chumbhot of Nagara Svarga, Bangkok

Wasters, through distortion, agglutination, or other accidents during the process of firing, sometimes assume fantastically pleasing shapes.

209. *Four-handled Jar*
H. 19 cm.
National Museum, Bangkok

Found in the old city of Sukhodaya during the course of excavations in 1955, this unglazed vessel is reminiscent of a Greek amphora.

210-217. *Examples of Chieng Mai ware (late Chieng Sèn) style, 15th and 16th centuries**

210. *Roof finial*
H. 21 cm.
National Museum, Bangkok

This finial in the form of a swan was made for the Library at Wat Pra Sing, Chieng Mai.

211. *Vase Decorated with Floral Motif*
H. 19.5 cm.

This vase from Gâ Long in the Province of Chieng Râi was probably made by a potter from Svargaloka who had been moved north during the wars between the Kingdoms of Ayudhyā and Chieng Mai. It also indicates a strong affinity with Chinese wares of the Tzu-ch'ou type.

212. *Jar*
H. 20 cm.

This example of Sân Gampèng ware was found at Bân Bâ Tung.

213. *Deep Dish with a Two-fish Motif*
D. 24.5 cm.
Sân Gampèng ware

214. *Plate with a Two-fish Motif*   (fig. 115)
D. 23 cm.
Sân Gampèng ware

215. *Plate with Lotus Motifs*
D. 25.5 cm.
Sân Gampèng ware

216. *Plate with Floral Motif*
D. 18.5 cm.
Sân Gampèng ware

*Note: With the exception of No. 210, all examples of Chieng Mai ceramics come from the collection of Mr. Kraiśrī Nimmānaheminda of Chieng Mai.

217. *Plate with Floral Motifs*
D. 27.5 cm.

Found at a Lawa village in the Province of Chieng Mai, this plate is probably an example of Wieng Gâ Long ware, and therefore made in the Province of Chieng Râi.

218-223. *Chinese export ware made for the Siamese market*

218. *Pentachromatic Bowl*   *(fig. 137)*
Porcelain. H. 8 cm.
National Museum, Bangkok
Ayudhyā style, 17th-18th century A. D.

In the 17th and 18th centuries many kinds of porcelains were made in China after Thai designs. This "Bencharong" or five-coloured pattern, with designs of mythological figures, animals and floral designs, and a green background inside the bowl, is typical of the Ayudhyā period.

219. *Bowl with Lid*
Porcelain. H. (with lid) 12.5 cm.
National Museum, Bangkok

This "golden" bowl is typical of a slightly later style than the preceding one. The main outer decoration remains Thai, but the inner part of the bowl is painted with a landscape in the Chinese manner.

220. *High Bowl with Lid*
Porcelain. H. (with lid) 17.5 cm.

221. *Tray*
Porcelain. H. 4.8 cm., D .10.5 cm.
National Museum, Bangkok

222. *Vase*
Porcelain. H. 23 cm.
National Museum, Ayudhyā

223. *Drum with Porcelain Handle*
H. 36 cm., D. 20 cm.
National Museum, Bangkok

The fact that this type of drum, called

"Thon," has a porcelain handle of intricate design in no way lessens its tonal quality.

VII. Objects in Wood

(224 — 241)

224. *Standing Buddha Image*   *(fig. 126)*
Wood. H. 99 cm.
Collection of Mr. James H. W. Thompson, Bangkok
Ayudhyā style, 17th-18th century A. D.

Some Ayudhyā Buddha images were made of wood but only a few of them antedate the 17th century. This figure was presumably carved by a Chinese artist. The facial features are typically Chinese with small and rather slanting eyes as well as pointed-up eyebrows. The body and the monastic robe of the Buddha are, however, in Thai style.

225. *Demon Figure*
Wood. H. 105 cm.
National Museum, Bangkok
Ayudhyā style, 17th-18th century A. D.

This demon figure, functioning as the guardian at the door to a place of worship, comes from Wat Champa, Chaiyâ, in the south of Thailand.

226. *Votive Tablet Stand*
Wood. H. 102 cm.
Collection of Prince Piyarangsit Rangsit, Bangkok
17th-18th century, A. D.

The framework of this tablet is made up of two intertwined six-headed *nāgas*, in the Chieng Sèn style. The eighteen clay Buddha images are in the Ayudhyā style.

227. *Model of a Vihāra*   *(fig. 122)*
Wood. H. 61 cm., L. 48 cm., w. 28 cm.
National Museum, Ayudhyā
Ayudhyā style, 17th-18th century

228. *An Angel in Adoration*
Wood. H. 80.5 cm.
National Museum, Bangkok
Bangkok style, late 18th-early 19th century
A. D.

This celestial being, also dressed in royal attire, is known as a "Tépnom."

229. *A Kinnarī*
Wood. H. 150 cm.
National Museum, Bangkok
Bangkok style, late 18th-early 19th century
A. D.

This mythological lady with avian extremities is dressed in royal attire. Such figures were used to adorn buildings or funeral pyres.

230. *A Mythological Animal*
Gilt wood. H. 62 cm., L. 100 cm.
National Museum, Bangkok
Bangkok style, late 19th-early 20th century
A. D.

231. *Model of a* Prăṅg
Wood on a bronze pedestal
H. (with pedestal) 60 cm.
National Museum, Bangkok
Bangkok style, 19th-20th century

232. *Carved Panel*
Wood. W. 59.5 cm., L. 109 cm.
Ayudhyā style, 17th-18th century A. D.

This carved panel was used as a back rest for a bench in a boat. Two *Kāla* heads, Chinese dogs, flames and floral motifs form part of the intricate design.

233. *Carved Door Panels*
Wood. H. 184 cm., W. 89 cm.
Bangkok style, late 18th century A. D.

This pair of carved doors probably came from a monastery. The decorative motifs used are celestial beings, *Garudas* and monkeys, as well as swans, *nāgas*, and two *Kāla* heads. The background is studded with pieces of opaque glass.

234. *Screen*
Wood. 171.5 x 178 cm. (including the frame)
Collection of Prince Sanid Prayurasakdi Rangsit, Bangkok
Ayudhyā or early Bangkok style, 18th-19th century A. D.

A carved screen such as this one is almost unique in Thai art. On the front panel a group of women, curiously arranged in the form of an elephant, stand in front of a gate. The back panel shows a hunting scene. The main motifs are Thai and Indian, and the treatment of the landscape is Chinese.

235. *Screen*
Mother-of-pearl inlaid on wood.
H. 68 cm., W. 63 cm.
National Museum, Bangkok
Bangkok style, middle of the 19th century

The Buddha is represented as preaching to the eighty chief disciples.

236. *Wall Bracket*
Wood. H. 158 cm., W. 54 cm.
National Museum, Bangkok
Chieng Mai (late Chieng Sèn) style,
18th-19th century

This bracket, carved with intertwined *nāgas*, was made for Wat Pra Sing in Chieng Mai.

237. *Covers for a palm-leaf Manuscript*
Wood covered with designs in gold.
L. 98.2 cm., W. 6 cm.
National Museum, Bangkok
Bangkok style, 19th century A. D.

238. *Flower Tray*
Wood. H. 23.5 cm., D. 37.5 cm.
Collection of
Mr. Kraiśrī Nimmānaheminda, Chieng Mai
Chieng Mai (late Chieng Sèn) style,
19th-20th century

239. *Gun-powder Receptacle*
Lacquered Wood. L. 18 cm.
Collection of

Mr. Kraiśrī Nimmānaheminda, Chieng Mai
Chieng Mai (late Chieng Sèn) style,
19th-20th century

The carved design mingles the form and
feathers of a bird with floral patterns.

240. *Coffer* *(fig. 159)*
Wood. H. 53.5 cm., W. 48 cm., L. 78.5 cm.
National Museum, Bangkok
Ayudhyā style, 17th-18th century

Originally a box in which to keep clothing,
this coffer, after being donated to a monastery, was used to store sacred manuscripts.
Its black and gold lacquer designs include
scenes from the *Rāmakirti* as well as various
mythological and zodiacal animals. The
designs were restored in 1925. (For a brief
description of lacquer painting see page 169)

241. *Decorated Book Cabinet* *(fig. 163)*
Wood. HT. 176 cm., W. 72 cm., L. 100 cm.
National Museum, Bangkok
Ayudhyā style, 17th-18th century A. D.

Cabinets such as this one were used in
monasteries to house sacred books. The front
and sides of this cabinet are decorated with
colors on black lacquer; the particular
episode depicted on the front is the capture
of the White Monkey-god, Hanuman, by the
sons of Rāma. The treatment of the animals
and of trees suggests some Chinese influence.
On the other hand, the two gold on black
angels on the back are typically Thai. (Cf.
page 169) .

VIII. Paintings

(242 — 263)

242. *Preaching Scene*
Painting on wood. 46 cm. x 63 cm.
(with frame)
Collection of Prince Piyarangsit Rangsit,
Bangkok

Bangkok style, late 18th or 19th century

A monk preaches to members of the royal
family, while a meal is being prepared to
present to him. The curtain in the background shows that the scene takes place in a
palace. The monk sits on a carpet, his hand
being stroked by a child. In the foreground
two boys prepare rice and "betel-nut", and
a child crawls towards his mother who holds
a food-container. In the center is a demon
who has joined the listeners, presumably in
the hope of learning how to mend his ways so
as to be reborn in better circumstances.

243. *Standing Buddha flanked by* *(fig. 154)*
two Disciples
Painting on cloth. 305 cm. x 101.5 cm.
Collection of Mr. James H. W. Thompson,
Bangkok
From Tonburî. Bangkok style,
early 19th century

The Buddha, standing on a pedestal and
under an arch which echoes the shape of his
halo, is attended by flying angels and two
disciples who stand beneath five-tiered umbrellas. At their feet are two demons and a
monkey. The lower register illustrates a scene
from the Vidhurajātaka, in which the demon
is trying to kill the Bodhisattva by tying him
to a horse's tail.

244. *The life of the Buddha*
Painting on cloth. 308 cm. x 109 cm.
Collection of Mr. James H. W. Thompson,
Bangkok
Bangkok style, early 19th century

This painting, from Subarnapurī, illustrates the principal episodes of the life of the
Buddha.

245. *The last ten lives of Buddha*
Painting on cloth. 393 cm. x 122 cm.
Collection of Mr. Adhara Śirikandaravara,
Bangkok
Bangkok style, 19th century

The subject matter of this painting is taken from the *jātaka* tales describing the ten previous lives of Buddha. In addition, at the bottom, there is depicted the story of Manohara and the seven *kinnarī* sisters. While bathing in a pond one of them is trapped by a hunter.

246. *The Buddha's Footprint*
Painting on cloth. 321 cm. x 200 cm.
Collection of Mr. A. B. Griswold, Tonburî
Bangkok style, 19th century

Footprint, with 108 auspicious signs (cf. page 98). At either side of the footprint, pictures of decaying corpses (a subject for mediation to remind the monk of the instability of life). Below: various holy monuments in Ceylon, with labels in Thai. An inscription at the bottom gives the date the painting was finished, equivalent to 1874.

247. *Scene from Vessantarajātaka*
Painting on paper. 74 cm. x 65 cm.
Collection of Mr. Kraiśrī Nimmānaheminda, Chieng Mai
Late Chieng Sèn style, 19th century

248. *(1) The Buddha preaching to his mother in heaven*
(2) The Descent from Heaven
Painting on cloth. 250.5 cm x 87 cm.
(with frame).
Collection of Mrs. C. Mangskau, Bangkok
Bangkok style, late 19th or early 20th century

The iconography may be compared with earlier treatments of these subjects in sculpture (Cf. page 157).

249. *Scene from Vessantarajātaka*
Painting on cloth. 55.5 cm. x 37.6 cm.
Collection of Mrs. C. Mangskau, Bangkok
Bangkok style, late 19th or early 20th century

Prince Vessantara gives away his deer-drawn chariot to four Brahmins, pouring water from a pot into their hands in testimony of the gift. (Cf. no. 107).

250. *Seated Buddhas in niches*
Painting on cloth. 50 cm. x 36.5 cm.
Collection of Mrs. C. Mangskau, Bangkok
Bangkok style, late 19th or early 20th century

Three figures of the Buddha *calling the Earth to witness*; the intervening compositions are lotus flowers arranged to suggest the face of the monster *Kāla*.

251. *The Buddha's return to Kapilavastu (fig. 155)*
Painting on wood. 100.5 cm. x 65 cm.
(with frame)
Collection of Prince Sanid Prayurasakdi Rangsit
Bangkok style,
late 19th or early 20th century

The Buddha preaches to his wife and child. *Genre* scene in the foreground, with gamblers, and a servant begging his master's forgiveness. Architecture of late 19th century; attendants and ordinary people dressed in the style of the period; guards in westernized uniforms; important personages dressed in classical style.

252. *Scene from Mahosatha Jātaka*
Painted on cloth. 42 cm. x 38 cm.
Collection of Mr. James H. W. Thompson
Bangkok style, late 19th or early 20th century

This painting illustrates the virtue of wisdom. The scene represents the episode when Mahosatha lures his enemies into a cave, puts out the light and threatens to kill them. The landscape shows some Chinese influence but the human figures are typically Thai.

253. *Painting Representing a Karen Hunting Scene*
Painted on cloth. 40.5 cm. 33 cm.
Collection of Mr. James H. W. Thompson
Bangkok
Bangkok style, early 20th century

Non-religious paintings are quite rare in

158. Fruits and flowers. Painting on wood. Sudarśana Monastery, Bangkok.

Below: 159. Gilt and lacquered chest. Wood; 58 cm. x 48 cm. x 78 cm. (Cat. no. 240.)

160. Heavenly Beings. Mural Painting in Wat Yai, Petburí.

161. Scene from the *Vessantarajātaka*. Mural painting in the Golden Monastery (Suvarnārāma), Tonburî.

162. Monastery scene. Mural painted about 1860 by command of King Mongkut. Great Relic Monastery, Bangkok.

Opposite: 163. Manuscript cabinet. Lacquered wood with paintings. Rear view shown here. Ht. 176 cm. (Cat. no. 241.)

Catalogue of the Exhibition

Notes by

M. C. Subhadradis Diskul

Chief Curator, National Museum, Bangkok

Note: While the material in the historical section is presented chronologically according to the table given on page 26, the objects in the Exhibition are listed by media. Historical sequence is followed within each category.

I. Images and Objects in Stone and Marble

(1 — 24)

1. *Wheel of the Doctrine, with Crouching Deer* (fig. 20)
Stone. Height of wheel: 72 cm.
National Museum, Bangkok. Probably from
Nagara Paṭhama
Dvāravatī style. 7th-8th century
Published: MNB, Pl. I; BAS, fig. 21; CSEA, fig. 37.

The Wheel of the Doctrine, together with a pair of crouching deer, symbolizes the Buddha's First Sermon, which was preached in the Deer Park near Benares. This kind of symbol appears in Indian art as early as the 3rd century B.C. In the view of many scholars its existence in Thailand confirms the opinion that Buddhism was introduced there as early as the reign of the Emperor Aśoka of India, although judging from the floral motifs carved on these stone wheels they themselves are of much later date. Connected with this one is a small figure of Sūrya, the sun-god, flanked by two dwarfs.

2. *Buddha* (fig. 12)
Stone. H. 108 cm.
National Museum, Ayudhyā. From the ruins
of the Great Relic Monastery, Lopburî
Dvāravatī style. 7th-8th century

The hands, now broken, were probably both performing the gesture of exposition, a combination which in Thailand is considered to represent the Descent from Heaven.

3. *Buddha Protected by the* Nāga's
Hood (fig. 16)
Stone. H. 75 cm.
National Museum, Bangkok
From Prācīnapurī
Dvāravatī style. 7th-8th century
Published: MNB, Pl. VI (misnumbered XI) ;
BAS, fig. 32; CSEA, fig. 45; AMD, fig. 494.

4. *Buddha with Indra and Brahmā,
Standing on a Fabulous Bird*
Stone. H. 40 cm.
National Museum. Ayudhyā
Dvāravatī style. 7th-8th century

The Buddha's hands were probably in the attitude of the Descent from Heaven. Some scholars think the bird on which the Buddha stands is Garuda or Vanasapati; others, noting that it has the beak of Garuda (the mount of Vishṇu), the horns of a bull (the mount of Śiva) and the wings of a wild goose (the mount of Brahmā), think it symbolizes the Hindu religions acknowledging the superiority of Buddhism.

5. *Head of a Buddha Image* (fig. 6)
Stone. H. 39 cm.
National Museum, Bangkok. Transferred
from the National Museum, Ayudhyā
7th-8th century
One of the finest examples of Dvāravatī art.
Published: MNB, Pl. VI (misnumbered XI);
AMD, fig. 353; TMB, fig. 94.

6. *Architectural Fragment* (fig. 5)
Stone. H. 60 cm.
National Museum, Bangkok. Found at
Brah Paṭhamacetiya, Nagara Paṭhama
Dvāravatī style. 7th-8th century
Published: AMD, figs. 323-327.

An aerial palace, with the god Sūrya and other personages peering out the windows.

7. *Standing Divinity* (fig. 31)
Stone. H. 98 cm.
National Museum, Bangkok. From Śri Deb
School of Śri Deb. 7th-8th century
Published: EOL, Pl. XI.

Judging from the headdress, this statue represents Vishnu; but the probable position of the left arm might suggest Kṛishṇa Govardhana.

8. *Vishṇu* (fig. 32)
Stone. H. 150 cm.
National Museum, Bangkok

From Vieng Sra
Malay Peninsula. 7th-8th century
Published: MNB, Pl. IX; Dupont in BEFEO
XLI/2, Pl. XXVIII; BAS, fig. 48; CSEA, fig. 51.

9. *Hands of Vishṇu?*
   Stone. H. 31.5 cm.
   National Museum, Bangkok
   From Pracīnapurī
   7th-8th century

10. *The Bodhisattva Avalokiteśvara
    (Lokeśvara)* *(fig. 33)*
    Stone. H. 45 cm.
    National Museum, Bangkok. From the
    province of Surāshṭradhānī
    Śrīvijaya style, 8th-9th century
    Published: MNB, Pl. XI (misnumbered VI) .

    The headdress contains a small figure of the
    Dhyāni Buddha.

11. *Buddha seated on the coiled body of the*
    Nāga
    Stone. H. 111 cm.
    National Museum, Bangkok. From the
    Great Relic Monastery, Ayudhyā
    Lopburî style. About 11th century

12. *Buddha* *(fig. 58)*
    Stone. H. 88 cm.
    National Museum, Lopburî. From the
    Great Relic Monastery, Lopburî
    Lopburî style. 13th-14th century

    The Buddha is seated in meditation, with
    folded legs.

13. *Head of a Buddha Image*
    Stone. H. 23 cm.
    National Museum, Bangkok. From the
    Great Relic Monastery, Lopburî
    Lopburî style. 12th-13th century
    Published: MNB, Pl. XXIX.

14. *Relief* *(fig. 47)*
    Red sandstone. H. 69 cm., L. 60 cm.
    National Museum, Bangkok
    From Caṇḍapurī
    Lopburî style. About 11th century

Three personages are seated in a pavilion,
two of them holding lotuses, one an indistinct
object. In the background are two others, one
of whom (the figure is broken away) holds a
fan.

15. *Antefix from the Roof of a Sanctuary*
    Stone. H. 69 cm.
    National Museum, Bangkok
    From Śrisakesa
    Lopburî style. 12th-13th century

    A divinity rides a bull with a single head
    and two bodies. Such figures are typical of
    the Lopburî school in Northeast Thailand.

16. *Column from a Temple*
    Stone. H. 116 cm.
    National Museum, Bangkok. Said to come
    from the temple of Pimâi
    Lopburî style. 11th-12th century

    On one side a door-guardian (dvārapāla)
    holding a club; on one side a celestial nymph
    (apsaras) holding a lotus.

17. *Carved Stone Slab*
    87 x 76 cm.
    National Museum, Bangkok. From the
    Monastery of the Abundant Bodhi Trees
    (Wat Sî Chum) , Sukhodaya
    Sukhodaya style. Late 13th or early
    14th century

    Carved in relief with a lotus design. Several
    such slabs, together with other slabs incised
    with drawings of the *Jātaka* tales, were dis-
    covered in re-use as ceiling-slabs in a narrow
    intramural stairway at this monastery, having
    apparently been placed there for safety rather
    than for exhibition. They may, therefore, be
    older than the monastery building.

18. *Pedestal for an Image*
    Stone. H. 45 cm.
    National Museum, Bangkok. From Payao,
    in the province of Chieng Râi, northern
    Thailand
    Chieng Sèn style. 15th-18th century

    Carved with donors (?) in the guise of

divinities, riding elephants and making offerings to the image, with attendants standing at corners (two of them carved in such a way that they seem to be a single person with two heads) .

19. *Head of a Buddha Image*
Stone. H. 36.5 cm.
National Museum, Lopburî. From the
Monastery of the Great Relic, Lopburî

Although the Thai usually preferred bronze to stone for sculpture, a large number of stone Buddha images were made during the Ayudhyā period. Until recently we have been inclined to attribute most of them to the 17th century, when Cambodia again became a vassal of Siam and the fashion of imitating Khmer art recommenced. Some stone images of this style, however, have been found in the crypt of Wat Rājapūraṇa at Ayudhyā, which was begun in 1424. This head might be considered to have been made before the 17th century (cf. page 142) .

20. *Head of a Buddha Image*
Stone, with traces of red lacquer. H. 32 cm.
National Museum, Lopburî. From the
Monastery of the Great Relic, Lopburî

This head, on the contrary, shows typical Ayudhyā characteristics and was probably made in the 17th century

21. *Bo Tree*   *(fig. 131)*
Stone. H. 48 cm.
National Museum, Bangkok. Discovered in
a canal at Ayudhyā
Ayudhyā style, 17th-18th century?

This kind of carving is extremely rare in Thai art, and this is the only example possessed by the National Museum. It was doubtless part of the background for a Buddha image.

22. *Boundary Stone* (sīmā)
H. 52 cm. W. 48 cm.
National Museum, Bangkok. From a
monastery at Candapurī

Bangkok style. Late 18th-early 19th century

One of a series used to surround the ordination-hall *(uposatha)* of a monastery. This one is carved with the figure of a divinity with palms pressed together in the gesture of respect, and holding a pair of lotuses.

23. *Relief*
Marble. 45.5 x 45.5 cm.
National Museum, Ayudhyā
Bangkok style. Mid-19th century

Fight between the monkey Sugrīb and the demon Kumbhakarṇa, an episode from *Rāmakirti* (Thai version of *Rāmāyaṇa*) . This slab is one of a large series carved during the reign of King Rāma III (1824-1851) . Most of them were installed at the Jetavanārāma (Wat Pó) , in Bangkok, but this one and its mate (no. 24) come from another monastery (in Ayudhyā) which was restored during the same reign.

24. *Relief*   *(fig. 148)*
Marble. 45.5 x 45.5 cm.
National Museum, Ayudhyā
Bangkok style. Mid-19th century

Unidentified scene; perhaps a fight between the monkey Hanuman and a demon. (See No. 23 above.)

II. Figures in Stucco and Terra Cotta
(25 — 51)

25. *Buddha*
Stucco. H. 32.5 cm.
National Museum, Bangkok

This image was discovered by students in archaeology in the University of Fine Arts during the course of excavations at Û Tòng. It is an example of late Dvāravatī art, perhaps around the 11th century, and is transitional to the Û Tòng style.

26-35. *Human and Animal Details from a Brick Monument*

These stucco ornaments are all in the Dvāravatī style, 6th to 11th century.

26. *Head of a Divinity*
H. 26 cm.
National Museum, Nagara Paṭhama

27. *Head of a Divinity* *(fig. 26)*
H. 12.5 cm.
National Museum, Nagara Paṭhama
The earring is typical of Dvāravatī art.

28. *Torso of a Divinity* *(fig. 30)*
H. 49 cm.
National Museum, Bangkok. From Braḥ Paṭhamacetiya, Nagara Paṭhama

29. *Head of a Demon*
H. 14 cm.
National Museum, Bangkok

30. *Head of a Divinity (Śiva?)*
H. 14 cm.
National Museum, Nagara Paṭhama

31. *Head of a Divinity* *(fig. 28)*
H. 15 cm.
National Museum, Nagara Paṭhama

32. *Head*
H. 9 cm.
National Museum, Nagara Paṭhama

33. *Animal Figure*
H. 22 cm.
National Museum, Nagara Paṭhama
This figure resembles one identified by P. Dupont (AMD. fig. 225) as a haṁsa, or swan.

34. *Animal Figure*
H. 20 cm.
National Museum, Nagara Paṭhama

35. *Animal Figure*
H. 19 cm.
National Museum, Nagara Paṭhama
The motif of the winged lion, originating in

Asia Minor, came to Southeast Asia by way of India.

36. *Head of a Buddha Image* *(fig. 29)*
Terra cotta. H. 21 cm.
Collection of Mr. A. B. Griswold, Tonburî
From Wat Kūkuṭa, Lampûn
Haripuñjaya style (offshoot of Dvāravatī)
13th century

37. *Buddhist Votive Tablet*
Terra cotta. H. 14.2 cm.
National Museum, Bangkok
From Rājapurī
Dvāravatī style. 7th-9th century
Published: SVT, Pl. III.

Pious persons used to fashion great numbers of votive tablets and bury them under stupas, as an act of merit and with the intent of causing the Buddhist religion to live beyond its allotted span of 5000 years. This tablet represents the Great Magical Display at Śrāvastī. The Buddha sits on a lotus held by a *nāga*, while *nāgas*, princes and divinities worship him. In the sky are figures of Sūrya and various celestials. On the back of the tablet appears the *Ye dhamma* inscription in *graṇṭha* characters.

38. *Bust of an Ogress* (yakshinī)
Terra cotta. H. 6.5 cm.
National Museum, Lopburî
Dvāravatī style. 9th-11th century

Several terra cotta figures of ogresses have been found at Nagara Paṭhama and Lopburî. This one, discovered at Lopburî, wears earrings that are dissimilar to each other. The left earring is typical of Dvāravatī art, the right resembles the later art of Lopburî.

39. *Torso*
Terra cotta. H. 9 cm.
National Museum, Lopburî
Dvāravatī style. 9th-11th century

Male figure, holding a monkey by a rope, the monkey snatching a fruit from a bunch held in the left hand of the figure. We do not know precisely the purpose of figurines like this. Perhaps they were toys for children, or else offerings to some deity.

40. *Torso. Male Figure, with an Animal (dog?) (fig. 27)*
Terra cotta. H. 7 cm.
National Museum, Lopburî
Dvāravatī style. 9th-11th century

41. *Votive tablet*
Clay. H. 12 cm.
National Museum, Bangkok. From Chaiyâ or Pattalung
Śrīvijaya style. 8th-13th century
Published: SVT, Pl. VIII, center.

In the center, the Buddha seated in the attitude of preaching, surrounded by divinities or Bodhisattvas. Inscribed with Sanskrit formula *Ye dharma . . .* in *nāgari* letters. In accordance with the practice in *Mahāyāna* countries, such votive tablets were often made of clay mixed with the ashes of some deceased priest who was held in high esteem.

42. *Votive Tablet*
Clay. H. 9.5 cm.
National Museum, Bangkok. From Trăng
Śrīvijaya style. 8th-13th century
Cf. SVT, Pl. VIII, upper left.

Figure of the four-armed Avalokiteśvara seated on a lotus.

43. *Mould and Impression*
Terra cotta. H. 9.3 cm.
National Museum, Bangkok
From Sukhodaya
Lopburî style. 13th-14th century
The Buddha with right hand performing the gesture of dispelling fear.

44. *Votive Tablet*
Terra cotta. H. 11.5 cm.
National Museum, Bangkok
From Nagara Paṭhama
Lopburî style. 13th-14th century
An identical tablet is published in SVT, Pl. VII.

45. *Head of a Buddha Image*
Stucco. H. 32.5 cm.
Collection of A. B. Griswold, Tonburî
Sukhodaya style. 15th century (?)

46. *Votive Tablet*
Terra cotta. H. 14.7 cm.
National Museum, Bangkok
From Svargaloka
Sukhodaya style. 14th century

This tablet represents a shrine containing an image of the Buddha calling the Earth to witness his victory over Māra, with a Bo tree in the background, and vases of flowers presented by worshipers.

47. *Standing Buddha Holding a Bowl. Flanked by Two Disciples in the Same Posture*
Terra-cotta. H. 37.5 cm.
National Museum, Nagara Paṭhama
Ayudhyā style, 17th-18th century

48. *Head of a Buddha Image*
Stucco. H. 22 cm.
National Museum, Lopburî
Ayudhyā style, 17th-18th century

49. *Head of Garuda*
Stucco. H. 26 cm.
National Museum, Lopburî
Ayudhyā style, 17th-18th century

50. *Red Tortoise*
Terra-cotta. H. 3 cm. L. 4.5 cm.
National Museum, Ayudhyā
Ayudhyā style, 17th-18th century

51. *Black Cat*
Terra cotta. H. 2.8 cm. L. 5 cm.
National Museum, Ayudhyā
Ayudhyā style, 17th-18th century

III. Bronze Figures and Heads

(52 — 107)

52. *Buddha* *(fig. 22)*
Bronze. H. 46.5 cm.
National Museum, Bangkok
Dvāravatī style. 6th-11th century
Published: AMD, fig. 437.

This attitude, with both hands performing the gesture of exposition, is frequent in Dvāravatī art, whereas in classical Indian art the Buddha performs a gesture with the right hand alone and the left hand holds the hem of the robe.

53. *Buddha* *(fig. 21)*
Bronze. H. 14 cm.
National Museum, Bangkok
Dvāravatī style. 6th-11th century
Published: MNB, Pl. V, AMD, fig. 505.

The Buddha sits in the "European" fashion, performing the gesture of exposition. Springing from his shoulders are the remains of a circular halo, now broken; the palm of each hand is inscribed with an auspicious network of lines in the form of a flower. The throne is supported by four lions.

54. *Buddha* *(fig. 23)*
Bronze. H. 16.3 cm.
National Museum, Bangkok
Dvāravatī style. 6th-11th century
Published: AMD, fig. 423.

The Buddha stands with the right hand performing the gesture of bestowing favors. The pedestal is modern.

55. *Bust of the Buddha* *(fig. 24)*
Bronze. H. 11.3 cm.
National Museum, Bangkok
Dvāravatī style. 6th-11th century

56. *Head of a Buddha Image*
Bronze. H. 17 cm.
National Museum, Nagara Paṭhama
Dvāravatī style. 6th-11th century
Published: AMD, fig. 424.

Behind the head are the remains of a halo, now broken.

57. *Buddha* *(fig. 34)*
Bronze. H. 28 cm.
National Museum, Bangkok. From the Great Relic Monastery, Chaiyâ
Śrīvijaya style. 8th-13th century

58. *The Bodhisattva Avalokiteśvara (Lokeśvara)* *(fig. 35)*
Bronze. H. 72 cm.
National Museum, Bangkok. From the Great Relic Monastery, Chaiyâ
Śrīvijaya style. 9th-10th century
Published: MNB, Pl. XVII, BK, Pl. XLVII.

One of the finest *Mahāyāna* bronzes found in Thailand. The profuse jewelry recalls South Indian and Javanese models. The headdress contains a small figure of the Dhyāni Buddha.

59. *The Bodhisattva Avalokiteśvara (Lokeśvara)*
Bronze. H. 21.2 cm.
National Museum, Bangkok
Śrīvijaya style. 8th-13th century

The attributes in the four hands are a rosary (upper R. H.), a lotus (lower R. H.), a book (upper L. H.), a water-bottle (lower L. H.). In the headdress there is a small figure of the Dhyāni Buddha.

60. *Tārā* *(fig. 36)*
Bronze, H. 18 cm.
National Museum, Bangkok
Śrīvijaya style. 8th-13th century

A divinity of the *Mahāyāna*, consort of Avalokiteśvara. The upper pair of hands hold attributes, probably a rosary and a book; the middle pair are in the attitude of meditation; the lower R. H. performs the gesture of bestowing favors, the lower L. H. is broken. The background is a partly broken disk edged with flames, representing a glory.

61. *Buddha   (fig. 53)*
Bronze. H. 64.7 cm.
National Museum, Bangkok
From Prācīnapurī
Lopburī style. 12th-13th century

The Buddha wearing the attire of Royalty performs the gesture of dispelling fear with both hands. The navel is inlaid with a small piece of colored glass.

62. *Buddha Image with Pedestal   (fig. 57)*
Bronze, H. 20 cm.
National Museum, Bangkok
Lopburī style. 13th-14th century

The Buddha sits on the coiled body of the *Nāga*. The elaborate pedestal has a row of lions supporting the upper platform.

63. *Tripartite Stand, with Three Buddha Images   (fig. 46)*
Bronze. H. 35 cm. L. 28 cm.
National Museum, Bangkok
From Udayadhānī Province
Lopburī style. 13th-14th century

The *Mahāyāna* distinguishes three "bodies" or forms of the Buddha Gautama: the mortal shape in which the Buddha manifested himself to the world of men, the "body of bliss" manifested to the Bodhisattvas and the eternal aspect of the Buddha's word. Perhaps this bronze represents such a trinity.

64. *Buddha Seated on the Coiled Body of the* Nāga   *(fig. 56)*
Bronze. H. 62 cm.
National Museum, Bangkok
Lopburī style. 13th century

The theme of the Buddha seated on the coiled body of the *Nāga* was popular in Khmer art and the Lopburī school, perhaps because the legendary founders of the Khmer royal dynasty were an Indian Brahmin and a *nāgī* princess. This figure holds a small bowl in the hands, perhaps signifying that it represents *Baishajyaguru*, the "Buddha as a Physician" who was so popular in the reign of Jayavarman VII of Cambodia.

65. *Five-headed Bodhisattva Avalokiteśvara (Lokeśvara)*
Bronze. H. 38.5 cm.
National Museum, Bangkok
Lopburī style. 13th-14th century

66. *Prajñāpāramitā   (fig. 54)*
Bronze. H. 18.2 cm.
National Museum, Bangkok
Lopburī style. 10th-11th century

This "divinity," is symbolically considered in the *Mahāyanā* to be the Mother of all the Buddhas. The right hand presumably held a lotus, and the left (which now appears to be performing the gesture of bestowing favors) probably held a book.

67. *Vishṇu*
Bronze. H. 58 cm.
National Museum, Bangkok
Lopburī style. 13th-14th century

The god held a disk (upper R. H.), a lotus (lower R. H.), an object which is now lost (upper L. H.), and a conch-shell (lower L. H.).

68. *Vishṇu Mounted on Garuda*
Bronze. H. 12.5 cm.
National Museum, Bangkok
Lopburī style. 13th-14th century

The god, mounted on the mythical bird Garuda, holds the usual attributes: disk (upper R. H.), lotus (lower R. H.), conch-shell (upper L. H.), club (lower R. H.).

69. *Viśvakarman   (fig. 55)*
Bronze. H. 11.3 cm.
National Museum, Bangkok. From Udòn
Lopburī style. 13th-14th century

Described in the *Mahābhārata* as "lord of the arts, executor of a thousand handicrafts, carpenter of the gods, fashioner of all ornaments, most eminent of artisans, who formed the celestial chariots of the deities, on whose craft men subsist, and whom they continually worship as a great and immortal god." As usual, his pose is the so-called Javanese position. His hands hold indistinct objects, presumably instruments of his craft.

70. *Tantric Female Divinity*
Bronze. H. 12.3 cm.
National Museum, Bangkok
Lopburî style. 13th-14th century

Female divinity, perhaps a Dakini, in dancing attitude. The objects held in the hands are perhaps a knife and a bell, utensils used in the rites of the Tantric Buddhists.

71. *Dancing Figure* *(fig. 50)*
Bronze. H. 10.3 cm.
National Museum, Bangkok
Lopburî style. 13th-14th century

Dancing figure, holding a pair of small drums (?). Perhaps a Tantric divinity; or else a heavenly nymph *(apsaras)*, one of those who were born from the Churning of the Sea of Milk.

72. *Head of a Demon*
Bronze. H. 19 cm.
National Museum, Bangkok
Lopburî style. 13th-14th century

The double line around the mouth indicates the demoniac character.

73. *Garuda with Nāga.* *(fig. 51)*
Bronze. H. 35.5 cm.
National Museum, Bangkok
Lopburî style. About 11th century

The King of Birds, here represented in rather human form, grasps his enemy, the *Nāga*, presumably with the intention of tearing him apart.

74. *Buddha* *(fig. 79)*
Bronze. H. 108 cm.
Jetavanārāma (Wat Pó), Bangkok
Published: TMB, Pls. 42, 43 and page 47, where it is referred to as "the Lady of Chieng Sèn."

This image has the inconography of the Early Chieng Sèn (lion) type: legs crossed, short flap of cloth over the left shoulder, and lotus finial on top of the head; but the sculptural style is that of Sukhodaya. We know from the records of the reign of King Rāma I (1782-1809) that hundreds of old images were rescued from the ruined cities and installed at this monastery during that reign, and this is undoubtedly one of them: a short inscription, scratched on the pedestal in the writing of that period, indicates that this piece is Number 112 from Sukhodaya. In addition to the scratched inscription, there is a longer one cast in the pedestal, and hence contemporary with the casting of the image, giving the name of the Princess-donor, *Brah Cau Mè Srī Mahā Tā*. It is undated, but is written in a Sukhodaya script which has been dated by an epigraphist at about 1350. Scholars who date the Early Chieng Sèn style in the 12th-13th century see this image as an example of its influence on the school of Sukhodaya, and date it in the late 13th or early 14 century. (Cf. pages 95-96 and 123-124)

75. *Seated Buddha* *(fig. 78)*
Bronze. H. 60 cm.
National Museum, Ayudhyā
Sukhodaya style. 14th century

76. *Reclining Buddha*
Bronze. H. 9.5 cm. L. 34 cm.
National Museum, Bangkok
Sukhodaya style. 14th century

77. *Walking Buddha*
Bronze. H. (including pedestal) 166 cm.
Monastery of the Fifth King (Peñcamapabitra), Bangkok
Sukhodaya style. 14th century

78. *Head of a Buddha Image*
Bronze. H. 67 cm.
National Museum, Bangkok
Sukhodaya style. 14th century

This head belonged to an image in Wat

Hong (Haṁsaratnārāma), Tonburî. The whole image had been covered with plaster in the early 19th century, and it was only when the plaster began to flake off that the bronze was discovered. Soon afterwards the head broke off and was stolen, but was retrieved by officials of the Fine Arts Department.

79. *Śiva*
Bronze. H. 149.5 cm.
National Museum, Bangkok
Sukhodaya style. 14th century

This statue of Śiva and that of his consort Umā (No. 80) are among the finest examples of Sukhodaya art of a non-Buddhistic nature.

80. *Umā* (*fig. 83*)
Bronze. H. 154 cm.
National Museum, Bangkok
Sukhodaya style. 14th century

81. *Buddha* (*fig. 100*)
Bronze. H. 58.5 cm.
Collection of Mr. Dhata Vanij Sampati, Bangkok
Chieng Sèn style. 12th-13th century?

The Buddha sits with crossed legs and has a short flap of cloth over the left shoulder. The finial surmounting the skull, now broken off, was doubtless in the form of a lotus. This image is an example of what has been called the "lion type"; its dating is a subject of debate among scholars. (Cf. page 126)

82. *Buddha* (*fig. 109*)
Bronze. H. 63 cm.
Monastery of the Fifth King (Peñcamapabitra), Bangkok
Chieng Sèn style (Chieng Mai "lion type")
Published DBINS, Pl. XII.

This is another example of Chieng Sèn art. The pedestal bears an inscription in Pali, consisting mostly of quotations from the Canon, together with a date equivalent to 1486 A. D.

83. *Buddha Marking his Footprints* (*fig. 111*)
Bronze. H. 46 cm.

National Museum, Bangkok
Published: DBINS, Pl. VI.

The pedestal bears an inscription with a date equivalent to 1482 A. D. The image is typical of the late Chieng Sèn style (Chieng Mai mixed type). (See page 125)

84. *Buddha* (*fig. 101*)
Bronze. H. 68 cm.
Monastery of the Fifth King (Peñcamapabitra), Bangkok
Chieng Sèn style (Chieng Mai mixed type).
15th-16th century. (Cf. page 123)

Unlike numbers 81 and 82, the Buddha sits with folded legs and has a long flap of cloth over the left shoulder as well as a flame-shaped finial on top of the head. These are features derived from Sukhodaya.

85. *Crowned Buddha* (*fig. 102*)
Bronze. H. 46.5 cm.
National Museum, Bangkok
Late Chieng Sèn style (Chieng Mai mixed type).
14th-16th century (?)
(Cf. page 125)
The Buddha wears the attire of royalty.

86. *Face of a Buddha Image* (*fig. 110*)
Bronze. H. 20 cm.
National Museum, Lampûn
Chieng Sèn style. 13th-14th century (but cf. page 126)

This is probably the face of an image of the same type as numbers 81 and 82. As its expression has the gentleness and sweetness of the Sukhodaya style, it probably belongs to a relatively late phase of the early Chieng Sèn.

87. *Kneeling Figure* (*fig. 112*)
Bronze. H. 31.5 cm.
National Museum, Bangkok
Chieng Sèn style. 15th-16th century

This probably represents a prince in the guise of a deity, originally holding a conch-shell (now missing) from which to pour water into the ground to attest the presentation of

Thai art. Most of them occur as small *genre* scenes at the bottom of large religious paintings. This one portrays a Karen hunting scene. Many Karens live in the hills on both sides of the frontier between Thailand and Burma.

254-258. *Five Paintings from the Summer Palace Lent by H. M. the King*

These paintings form part of a group executed in a competition commanded by King Chulalongkorn. They were first exhibited at the Royal Cremation of his wife and children in 1887. Each painting is accompanied by a poem composed by the King and court poets dealing with the same subject. These works, painted on canvas, successfully blend the Thai tradition with Western pictorial conventions. They are on view in the reception rooms of the Varobhāsha Vimāna Pavilion at the Summer Palace, Bang Pa-in.

254. *King Nareśvara in Battle*
99 cm. x 71 cm. (with frame)

This painting represents the episode in the late 16th century when King Nareśvara and his younger brother, each sitting on the neck of an elephant, drove their mounts into the Burmese vanguard, and during which the king killed the Burmese crown prince in a duel. The officer seated on the howdah on the back of an elephant hands a needed weapon to the king and gives signals to the infantry to advance or retreat on orders from the king. The mahout or driver is at the back.

255. *King Rāma I Attacking the Burmese Camp at Tavoy*
104 cm. x 76 cm. (with frame)

This painting represents the scene when King Rāma I with his army attacked the Burmese camp at the town of Tavoy in the late 18th century. The elephants in this painting are war-elephants, without howdahs and white-tiered umbrellas on their backs, unlike the ceremonial ones represented in No. 254. The Thai generals on horses are protected by red umbrellas.

256. *Scene in the Himavanta Forest*
144 x 91 cm. (with frame)

257. *Scene from the Play Inao: the Burning of the City*
100 cm. x 69 cm. (with frame)

King Rāma II, who reigned between 1809 and 1824, composed a play, based on the Javanese legend about the hero Inao. The scene pictured here represents the abduction of the heroine, Pushpā, and the burning of her father's city of Daha, by Inao.

The artist has depicted a royal palace of King Chulalongkorn's time, and the Westernized fire-brigade and hoses which he introduced.

258. *Another Scene from the Play Inao: Cockfighting*
94.5 cm. x 63.5 cm. (with frame)

Cockfighting is depicted in the Javanese city of Dalang, the architecture of which looks oddly Victorian.

Illuminated Manuscripts

(259 — 263)

THE PRACTICE of illustrating sacred and other texts was derived from Indian models, which also influenced the format of the manuscripts. The earlier ones were long and narrow strips of palm leaf, in loose sequence. Later ones use the accordion pleat method, which permitted the use of both sides. The illustrations were placed in a variety of ways: a "page" might consist of the two halves of a fold and the picture placed either in the middle, the sides or sometimes even filling the entire space. In other cases three or more half-folds of the paper would be stretched open, and the picture would assume fairly large proportions. As each manuscript was an individual creation, the relation of text to image also varied to fit a particular case.

Most of the manuscripts are contained within a top and bottom pair of bindings, usually of leather. Especially important works were given covers with elaborate designs in wood, mother-of-pearl or carved ivory. (Cf. nos. 237, 286 and 287.)

The five manuscripts on display were lent by the Vajirañān Library, Bangkok.

259. *Manuscript on Military Strategy*
L. 130 cm., w. 36 cm.
Bangkok style, 1815

260. *Manuscript on Buddhism*
L. 977 cm., w.39 cm.
Bangkok style,
late 19th-early 20th century
This manuscript is one of the best of its kind. An allegory on Buddhism, it was intended to teach people to realize that living creatures are made up of five aggregates: bodily form, sensation, perception, thought, and consciousness; and that these five aggregates are impermanent, not self-contained, and cause sorrow. Some of the paintings describe episodes in the life of the Buddha.

261. *Manuscript* Representing
Fighting Scenes from the *Rāmakirtī*
L. 1356 cm., w. 47 cm.
Bangkok style,
late 19th-early 20th century
The figures represented are Rāma and Lakshmana, the heroes of the Rāmāyaṇa, fighting against demons; fighting and dancing between angels; and monkeys fighting against demons or with one another.

262. *Royal Manuscript on Massage*   *(fig. 156)*
L. 644 cm., w. 35 cm.
Bangkok style, 1871 A. D.
In 1871 King Chulalongkorn commanded

the chiefs of his medicine section and the scribe section to compose texts on medicine for the use of the public. This treatise gives anatomical charts with instructions on how to cure different diseases by massage.

263. *Manuscript on Siamese Cats and Birds*   *(fig. 157)*
L. 920 cm., w. 36 cm.
Bangkok style,
late 19th-early 20th century
The Thai people enjoy bringing up domestic animals. This manuscript is a set of poems describing various characteristics of cats and certain kinds of birds, with appropriate illustrations.

IX. Miscellaneous Objects

a) Textiles: 264-268
b) Theatrical arts: 269-280
c) Mother-of-Pearl: 281-286
d) Ivory: 287-288
e) Models: 289, 290
f) Crystal: 291-295

264-268. *Royal Silks*
A GROUP of brocaded or embroidered silk panels used as vestments by Court Ladies. They are all in the Bangkok style of the late 19th century. Three of them were woven in Thailand, one in India and the other in China.
National Museum, Bangkok
(except for No. 267)

264. *Embroidery*
Thai silk. L. 329 cm., w. 95.5 cm.

265. *Embroidery*
Thai silk. L. 256.6 cm., w. 84.5 cm.

266. *Brocade*
Thai silk. L. 376 cm., w. 161 cm.

267. *Embroidery*
Woven in India. L. 266 cm., w. 86.5 cm.
The Paribatra family collection, Bangkok.

This is an example of the work done in Gujarat for the Paribatra family, on Thai designs.

268. *Brocade*
L. 312 cm., w. 95.5 cm.

Made in Shanghai after Thai designs.

269-280. *These objects are all in the Bangkok style of the late 19th and early 20th centuries.*

269. *Shadow-play Figure*   *(fig. 149)*
Representing the God of Thunder
Leather. H. 145 cm., w. 124 cm.
National Museum, Bangkok

The shadow-play, or *Nang*, is probably derived from very ancient Hindu precedents. Its technique requires the manipulation before a white screen of large figures cut out of cow-hide. Individual personages, sometimes in pairs, from the principal legends — especially the *Rāmāyaṇa*, or its Thai version, the *Rāmakirti* — form the "troupe." For daylight performances there are painted figures; at night the forms move before a lighted screen. The actors who hold them aloft by two poles show their backs to the audience.

270. *Shadow-play Figure Representing Mekhalā*
Leather. H. 147.5 cm., w. 112 cm.
National Museum, Bangkok

Mekhalā, Goddess of Lightning, holds a crystal with which she teases the God of Thunder. He will throw his axe at her, causing thunder to strike lightning from her crystal.

271. *Shadow-play Figure Representing Rāma*
Leather. H. 159 cm., w. 60 cm.
National Museum, Bangkok

Rāma, the hero of the *Rāmāyaṇa*, is the eponymous ancestor of the present Royal dynasty of Thailand.

272. *Shadow-play Figure Representing Sita*
Leather. H. 149 cm., w. 112 cm.
National Museum, Bangkok

Sita is the consort of Rāma. Both of them are shown walking on *nāgas*.

273. *Marionette Representing Rāma*
Wood. H. 37 cm.
National Museum, Bangkok

The arms and legs of Thai marionettes are manipulated by strings from below, and the head is turned by a rod which goes through the body. This set of puppets originally belonged to H. R. H. Prince Pavaravijayañāna Heir-Apparent during the reign of King Chulalongkorn, and famed for his artistry.

274. *Marionette Representing Sita*
Wood. H. 34 cm.
National Museum, Bangkok

275. *Marionette Representing Rāvana*
Wood. H. 35 cm.
National Museum, Bangkok
Rāvana, the chief demon in the *Rāmakirti*, has ten heads and twenty arms. He is normally given a green complexion.

276. *Marionette Representing Sugrīb*
Wood. H. 34 cm.
National Museum, Bangkok

Sugrīb, the King of the Monkeys in the *Rāmakirti*, normally has a red complexion.

277. *Mask of Lakshmana, the Younger Brother of Rāma*   *(fig. 150)*
Paper. H. 68 cm.

In the private collection of His late Royal Highness Prince Nariśarānuvaptivaṁśa. Lent by his family, the Chitrabongs family. The mask-dance is presumably descended from the shadow-play. The performance is a mimed dance accompanied by music and singing.

278. *Mask of Rāvana*
Paper. H. 64 cm.

In the private collection of His late Royal Highness Prince Narisra Nuvadtivongs. Lent by his family, the Chitrabongs family.

279. *Mask of Birāb, a Demon*
Paper, H. 20 cm., W. 14 cm.
Lent by the Musical Division,
Department of Fine Arts

This mask was probably made during the second reign of Bangkok, in the first quarter of the 19th century, when Thai theatrical art reached its climax. Birāb is a demon who fights with Rāma in order to get the latter's wife, Sita, but is at last killed by Rāma.

280. *Mask of Hanuman, a Chief White Monkey*
Hard paper decorated with mother-of-pearl
H. 25 cm., W. 15 cm.
The Musical Division,
Department of Fine Arts

Hanuman, the chief white monkey in the *Rāmakirtī*, is sometimes more important than Rāma himself. His mask here is made of mother-of-pearl and one can notice in his mouth a symbol of the moon surrounded by stars, which appears when Hanuman yawns in order to show his magical power.

---

281. *A Monk's Alms-bowl with the Cover and Stand in Mother-of-Pearl Inlaid Work*
Metal. D. of bowl 29.5 cm.
National Museum, Bangkok
Bangkok style, 19th-20th century

The alms-bowl is traditionally of iron, but its stand and cover may be as elaborate as desired.

282. *Food Receptacle (fig. 151)*
Mother-of-pearl inlaid work
H. 57 cm., W. 46 cm.
National Museum, Bangkok
Bangkok style, 19th-20th century

This mother-of-pearl receptacle for food is indented at six corners. Its cover is decorated in Thai designs including *Kāla* faces and lions, which might denote that this household article formerly belonged to the Min-

istry of the Interior. The finial of the cover is a knob of mother-of-pearl intersected with red lacquered wood. The body of the receptacle is also inlaid with mother-of-pearl in Thai designs, lions, and *Kāla* faces, but the base is decorated with designs as if it were the foot of a table.

283. *Ecclesiastical Fan*
Cloth with mother-of-pearl inlaid on handle
H. 89 cm.
National Museum, Bangkok
Bangkok style, 19th-20th century

284. *Ecclesiastical Fan*
Embroidered cloth. H. 128 cm.
National Museum, Bangkok
Bangkok style,
late 19th or early 20th century

285. *Ecclesiastical Fan*
Embroidered cloth. H. 98.5 cm.
National Museum, Bangkok

286. *Covers for a Palm-leaf Manuscript*
Mother-of-pearl inlaid work
L. 55.5 cm., W. 6 cm.
National Museum, Bangkok
Bangkok style, 19th century

287. *Covers for a Palm-leaf Manuscript*
Ivory. L. 58.5 cm., W. 5.5 cm.
National Museum, Bangkok
Bangkok style

288. *Model of a Throne*
Ivory. H. 31 cm.
Collection of H. R. H.
Prince Bhanubandhu Yugala, Bangkok
Bangkok style, late 19th-early 20th century

289. *Model of an Orchestra Set*
Wood
Collection of H. R. H.
Princess Chumbhot of Nagara Svarga,
Bangkok

The typical Thai orchestra consists of nineteen instruments including drums, cymbals, xylophones, pipes, gongs, and a stringed instrument.

290. *Model of the Royal Barge*
Gilt wood. L. 238 cm.
National Museum, Bangkok

The royal barge is named "Śrī Subarnahaṁsa" because its prow is in the shape of a swan, the mount of the God Brahmā. The barge is used by the King in important ceremonies such as the procession on the Chao Phya River after the coronation, or the annual presentation of robes to monasteries. Rowed by forty-odd paddlers in red uniforms, the barge has a throne on a dais; further emblems of royalty are a parasol, a fan, a sun-shade and three-tiered umbrellas. It is actually more than sixty feet from tip to tip.

291-295. *Objects in Crystal*

OWING TO the construction of Phumipol Dam in Northwestern Thailand, a large part of that territory is expected to be permanently submerged. The Department of Fine Arts of Thailand has undertaken to preserve and remove as many of the monuments and works of art as possible. Much excavation in old stupas and *cetiyas* has already been accomplished. A small portion of sixteenth and seventeenth century crystal objects from Wats in the region of Chieng Mai dug up in February 1960 has been lent to the Exhibition. Crystal work is exceedingly rare except in Northern Thailand, since the mineral comes from Burma or Yunnan. The practice of this craft in this area is undoubtedly an instance of the relatively infrequent influence of China on Thai art. All the objects are lent by the National Museum, Bangkok; they are all in the Late Chieng Sèn style.

291. *Buddha Calling the Earth to Witness*
H. 5 cm.

Found at Wat Sî Kong, District of Hòt, Chieng Mai.

292. *A Two-Headed Swan*
L. 5 cm.
Found at Wat Sî Kong, District of Hòt, Chieng Mai.

This unusual animal form, whose symbolic meaning is unknown, is actually a container for relics.

293. *A Frog*
L. 6 cm.
Found at Wat Sî Kong, District of Hòt, Chieng Mai.

This frog, with rubies set in its eyes, is probably a fertility symbol but was also used as a container for relics.

294. *A Crouching Goat*
H. 5 cm., L. 9 cm.
Found at Wat Dòk Ngön, District of Hòt, Chieng Mai.

The form of this relic holder is presumably dictated by the year of the donor's birth. The year of the Goat is the seventh in the twelve-year cycle.

295. *Small Bowl with Lid*
H. 3 cm.
Found at Wat Dòk Kam, District of Hòt, Chieng Mai.

This bowl is also a receptacle for relics.

The exhibition is supplemented by 80 enlargements of photographs of monuments and archaeological sites in Thailand. Fifty in color were made from transparencies furnished by Ewing Krainin, Donald H. Rochlen, Elizabeth Lyons, and others, and thirty in black-and-white were made from negatives supplied by Alexander B. Griswold and the Archaeological Survey of Thailand.

Bibliography

ALABASTER *The Wheel of the Law* (London, 1871).

PRINCE BIDYALANKARANA *The Buddha's Footprint* (JSS XXVIII).

BLACK *The Lofty Sanctuary of Khao Phra Vihar* (JSS XLIV).

BOISSELIER *La statuaire khmère et son évolution* (Saïgon, 1955).

BORIBAL AND GRISWOLD *Sculpture of Peninsular Siam* (JSS XXXVIII).

BRIGGS *The Ancient Khmer Empire* (Philadelphia, 1951).

M. C. CHAND AND
KHIEN YIMSIRI *Thai Monumental Bronzes* (Bangkok, 1957).

COEDÈS *Bronzes khmèrs* (Paris, 1923).

COEDÈS *Documents sur l'histoire politique et religieuse du Laos Occidental* (BEFEO XXV).

COEDÈS *The Excavations at P'ong Tük* (JSS XXI).

COEDÈS *Les Etats hindouisés d'Indochine et d'Indonésie* (Paris, 1948).

COEDÈS *Les collections archéologiques du Musée National de Bangkok* (Paris, 1948).

COEDÈS *Note sur une statue de princesse siamoise* (JSS XVI).

COEDÈS *Pour mieux comprendre Angkor* (Paris, 1947).

DÖHRING *Art and Art Industry in Siam* (Bangkok, n.d.).

DÖHRING *Buddhistische Tempelanlagen in Siam* (Berlin, 1916).

DÖHRING *Kunst und Kunstgewerbe in Siam* (Berlin, n.d.).

DUPONT *L'Archéologie mône de Dvāravatī* (Paris, 1959).

DUPONT *La statuaire pré-Angkorienne* (Ascona, 1955).

DUPONT *Le Buddha de Grahi et l'école de Chaiyâ* (BEFEO XLII).

DUPONT *Vishnu mitrés de l'Indochine occidentale* (BEFEO XLI).

FEROCI *Aesthetics of Buddhist Sculpture* (JSS XXXVIII).

FEROCI *Traditional Thai Painting* (JSS XL).

FOURNEREAU *Le Siam ancien* (Paris, 1908).

GRISWOLD   *A Warning to Evildoers* (Artibus Asiae, xx/1).

GRISWOLD   *An Unusual Siamese Bronze* (Artibus Asiae, xxi/1).

GRISWOLD   *Buddha Images of Northern Siam* (JSS XLI).

GRISWOLD   *Dated Buddha Images of Northern Siam* (Ascona, 1957).

HUTCHINSON   *Sacred Images in Chiengmai* (JSS XXVIII).

HUTCHINSON   *The Seven Spires* (JSS XXXIX).

LALOUBERE   *Du royaume de Siam* (Paris, 1691).

LALOUBERE   *A New Historical Relation of the Kingdom of Siam* (London, 1693).

LEMAY   *A Visit to Sawankalok* (JSS XIX).

LEMAY   *Buddhist Art in Siam* (Cambridge, 1938).

LEMAY   *The Culture of South-East Asia* (London, 1954).

LEMAY   *On Tai Pottery* (JSS XXXI).

KRAISRI NIMMANAHEMINDA   *Sangambaeng glazed potteries* (JSS XLIII).

PRINCE DHANI NIVAT   *Inscriptions of Wat Phra Jetubon* (JSS XXVI).

PRINCE DHANI NIVAT   *The reconstruction of Rāma I* (JSS XLIII).

NOTTON   *Annales du Siam* (Paris, 1926-32).

QUARITCH WALES   *The Origins of Sukhodaya Art* (JSS XLIV).

PHYA ANUMAN RAJATHON   *The Golden Meru* (JSS XLV).

PHYA ANUMAN RAJATHON   *Phra Cedi* (JSS XL).

SEIDENFADEN   *An Excursion to Lopburî* (JSS XV).

SEIDENFADEN   *An Excursion to Phimâi* (JSS XLIV).

SPINKS   *Siam and the Pottery Trade of Asia* (JSS XLIV).

VAN VLIET   *Description of Siam* (JSS VII).

VAN VLIET   *Historical Account of Siam in the 17th century* (JSS XXX).

WELLS   *Thai Buddhism, its Rites and Activities* (Bangkok, 1939).

WOODS   *History of Siam* (Bangkok, 1933).

Index

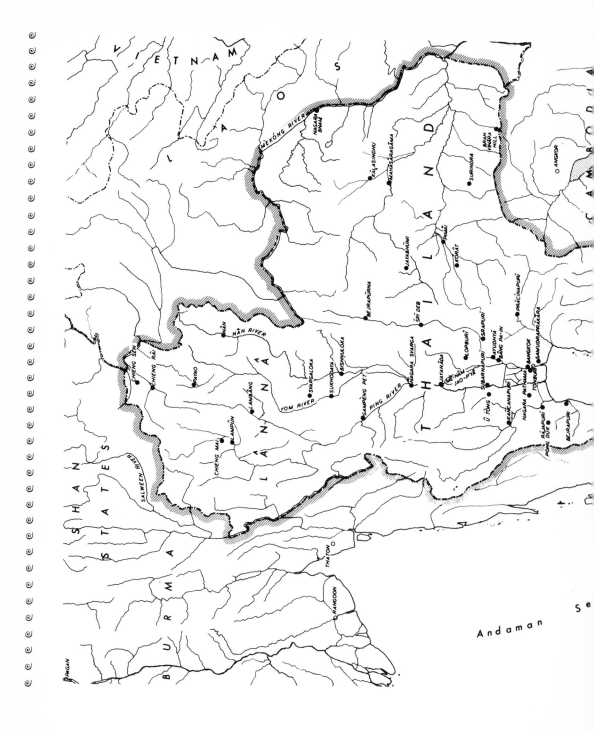

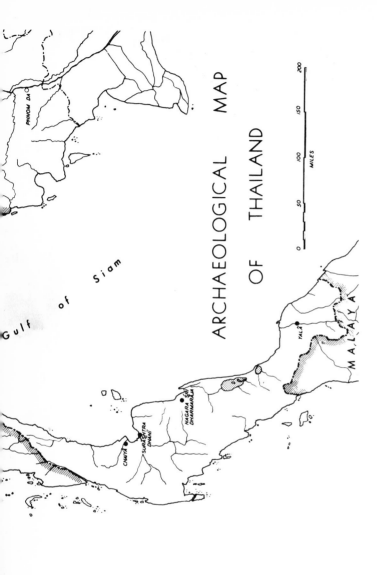

ARCHAEOLOGICAL MAP

OF THAILAND

Archaeological Map of Thailand

Type set in Linotype Baskerville by Capital City Press, Montpelier, Vt.
Stempel type ornament from Amsterdam Continental, New York
Printed offset on Mohawk Superfine 70 lb. by Meriden Gravure Co., Meriden, Conn.
Bound by Russell-Rutter Co., Inc., New York